EVOLUTION AND INTELLIGENT DESIGN IN A NUTSHELL

EVOLUTION AND INTELLIGENT DESIGN IN A NUTSHELL

THOMAS Y. LO, PAUL K. CHIEN,

ERIC H. ANDERSON, ROBERT A. ALSTON,

ROBERT P. WALTZER

SEATTLE   DISCOVERY INSTITUTE PRESS   2020

Description

Are life and the universe a mindless accident—the blind outworking of laws governing cosmic, chemical, and biological evolution? That's the official story many of us were taught somewhere along the way. But what does the science actually say? Drawing on recent discoveries in astronomy, cosmology, chemistry, biology, and paleontology, *Evolution and Intelligent Design in a Nutshell* shows how the latest scientific evidence suggests a very different story.

Copyright Notice

Library Cataloging Data

Evolution and Intelligent Design in a Nutshell by Thomas Y. Lo, Paul K. Chien, Eric H. Anderson, Robert A. Alston, and Robert P. Waltzer

Library of Congress Control Number: 2020936755

168 pages, 6 x 9 x 0.4 in. & 0.5 lb, 229 x 152 x 9 mm & 237 g

ISBN-13 Paperback: 978-1-936599-81-3, Kindle: 978-1-936599-83-7, EPub: 978-1-936599-82-0

BISAC: SCI015000 SCIENCE / Cosmology

BISAC: SCI008000 SCIENCE / Life Sciences / Biology

BISAC: SCI027000 SCIENCE / Life Sciences / Evolution

BISAC: SCI075000 SCIENCE / Philosophy & Social Aspects

Publisher Information

Discovery Institute Press, 208 Columbia Street, Seattle, WA 98104

Internet: http://www.discoveryinstitutepress.com/

Published in the United States of America on acid-free paper.

First Edition, First Printing, May 2020.

CONTENTS

Acknowledgments

At a recent science seminar, I (Thomas Y. Lo) shared my desire to provide an up-to-date, easy-to-read guide to origins science, a book exploring some of the exciting discoveries that are reinvigorating the conversation about how life and the universe came to be. Soon I had help from three of my fellow attendees and another colleague, each an able communicator and each focused on a different part of the origins landscape: electrical engineer Robert Alston, software engineering executive and design theorist Eric Anderson, biology professor Robert Waltzer, and marine biology professor Paul Chien.

My deepest appreciation goes out to each of the four men above. And a special thanks goes to Eric, co-editor and contributing author, and to co-editor Jonathan Witt, whose energy and experience guided the project to completion. We also are grateful to Brian Gage for the cover design, and to Mike Perry for the layout and indexing.

Numerous hours and drafts and revisions go into producing any book, and our thanks also go out to the many colleagues, content reviewers, and proofreaders who have remained anonymous. Any mistakes that remain are our own.

Our thanks also go out to our families for their support during this undertaking and to you, the reader, for your willingness to embark with us on this journey of discovery.

INTRODUCTION

Thomas Y. Lo

WHERE DID WE COME FROM? HOW DID LIFE EMERGE IN THE FIRST place? Was there a beginning of the universe? How did it come to be? I long wrestled with these sorts of questions. But even as I was falling in love with modern science, I remained unaware of some recent scientific discoveries that cast fresh light on these ancient mysteries.

I was born in Nanjing, China, the third of four children. When I was two years old our family moved to Taipei, Taiwan, where I spent my childhood and early teenage years. My mother was a homemaker who later studied accounting and worked in a private all-girls high school to help with the family income. My father was a strict military officer who brought his workplace standards of discipline and rigor into the home. Family life was stressful and we dared not disobey or disappoint my father. When I was about ten years old, my family embraced Christianity, bringing with it a softening of my father's approach and a positive change in our family environment. This was a good time for our family.

At the age of twelve, I attended a church retreat. There were more than one hundred people in attendance, ranging in age from 11 to 82, including college students, young professionals, and retirees. In the last evening of the week-long program, the entire congregation underwent an unforgettable spiritual experience. As a result, I eventually decided to be baptized. However, even though I felt I had experienced a genuine spiritual experience in my own life, perhaps even a small miracle, I remained skeptical of the miracles in the Bible. They seemed too big, too grand, too different from the experiences of my own life. Could they really be true? If the events related in the Old Testament and the New

Testament weren't based on objective scientific evidence, how could they be credible?

As I went through my teenage years, the doubts only grew stronger with time. Classmates teased me about my faith. Teachers made condescending remarks about Christianity. I found it all very uncomfortable and irritating.

After I started college, this growing internal tension drove me away from my Christian faith. Externally I was still going through the motions, but internally I was not committed. I was living at home at the time, still having to go to church with my family and attend Christian fellowship groups on campus. It was tearing me apart emotionally. There was no joy in my life.

At the same time, I became deeply troubled by the big questions: What is the meaning of life? Why am I here? What am I supposed to do with my life? I immersed myself in the literatures of existentialism and Buddhism. Without finding any satisfactory answers, I sometimes felt frustrated and depressed. My quest for meaning and purpose didn't end, but I began to look for answers outside of the spiritual and religious realm. It didn't take long before I found the answers I was searching for.

Or at least I thought I had.

When I took modern physics in my third year of college, my professor described how electrons, protons, and neutrons behave in an atom. I immediately fell in love with it. The resemblance[1] between the numerous galaxies revolving in the enormity of space and the simple model my professor shared of the infinitesimal elementary particles orbiting in an atom captivated me.

Having found my passion in science and engineering, I set aside the big questions. My study of astronomy, geology, genetics, and the history of science in my later years, however, eventually led me back to them.

Yes, science led me back to the big questions, and I was in good company. About thirty-five years before my physics class, Albert Einstein found himself struggling to hold onto his belief in a static and eternal universe, one that was not created but had always existed. However, he felt compelled to revise his views after learning about several lines of new evidence, including the Doppler-like redshift of distant galaxies discovered by Edwin Hubble and other astronomers.

In January 1931, Hubble invited Einstein to visit California's Mt. Wilson Observatory to view Hubble's work on the redshift phenomenon. Perhaps the most famous photograph of the event shows Einstein peering through the eyepiece of the massive 100-inch Hooker Telescope,[2] then the world's largest. This now-famous scene of Einstein gazing up at the distant heavens while Hubble stands immediately behind him, a solemn look on his face and pipe in hand, was more of a media "photo op" than an actual scientific observation, but the image has come to represent both the reality of the expanding universe, and Einstein's willingness to embrace the evidence and follow it wherever it leads, even when it challenged his prior views.

The receding galaxies that generate the redshifts implied a beginning moment of the universe—what has come to be known as the Big Bang, and which seems to point to a dramatic creation event. I now wonder why the implications of this extraordinary finding—and in particular, the way that it upended the conventional scientific wisdom of an eternal universe—was not emphasized in my college textbooks or mentioned in my classrooms. Had I known about this powerful cosmological evidence of creation *ex nihilo* (creation out of nothing), would my struggle with the big questions have been less painful? I can't help but wonder.

The discovery that the universe did indeed have a beginning was followed by a series of discoveries in physics, chemistry, and astronomy showing that the laws and constants of physics and chemistry are narrowly fine-tuned to allow for life in the universe—to such a precise degree that it has the strong appearance of intention behind it.

One Nobel Prize-winning astronomer, Arno Penzias, put it this way: "Astronomy leads us to a unique event, a universe which was created out of nothing, one with the very delicate balance needed to provide exactly the conditions required to permit life..."[3]

Although these discoveries are more widely known today than they were thirty or forty years ago, many people are still unaware of the details or their potential implications. Even if science textbooks mention the Big Bang or the fine tuning of the universe, they often do so in a cursory and one-sided manner that downplays their significance. It's as if the textbook authors don't want their audience to open the door and walk through. That's unfortunate, because the evidence on the other side of the door is fascinating. It's charged with hints about our origins, and about what may have existed before and may exist beyond the universe. We'll walk through that door and take a look around, beginning in the next chapter.

Information and the Origin of Life

IN THE twentieth century, while physicists and cosmologists were unraveling some of the mysteries of the universe, scientists in other fields were busy puzzling out the mystery of information and its implications for the origin of living things. It's a story with one foot in biochemistry and another in computer science.

In 1948, five years after the first vacuum-tube computer was built, the transistor was invented by three physicists: John Bardeen, William Shockley, and Walter Brattain. That same year Claude Shannon published "A Mathematical Theory of Communication,"[4] which provided key insights into what would later become known as information theory. Shannon also introduced the word "bit" as a basic unit of information in computing and communications. Both of these developments helped propel the electronics industry to the present digital age. Little did these scientists know, however, that the digital age they ushered in would one day help us understand biological systems and provide insights into one of the key questions I had wondered about in my college days: the origin of life.

In 1952 Rosalind Franklin, at King's College, London, did ground-breaking work examining DNA's structure by X-ray crystallography. Based in part on Franklin's work, James Watson and Francis Crick made the now famous discovery that DNA is shaped like a twisting ladder, what is known as a double helix.

In addition to the helical structure, Watson and Crick proposed that the four types of nucleic acids—abbreviated as A, T, C, and G—would line up exclusively in A-T and C-G pairs. This elegant chemical structure suggested to Watson and Crick a "possible copying mechanism" for DNA,[5] with the long DNA molecule containing numerous possible sequences of A-T and C-G pairs that could carry hereditary information. Watson and Crick turned out to be right on both counts, and their discovery marked a turning point in our understanding of every living organism.

Further research confirmed that DNA and other molecules in the cell respond, not randomly, but purposefully, somewhat like a micro-computer executing machine instructions. The cell even has repair systems to fix DNA that has been damaged by external forces, akin to an error correction algorithm in a software program.

The discoveries of DNA's structure and the cell's information processing and repair systems forever changed our understanding of life's origin. With the Big Bang, mass and energy had emerged. Yet with no genetic information or digital codes, how was information generated to build life in the first place? This question has bedeviled the origin-of-life field ever since. Chapters 2 and 3 explore the question, and compare some of the competing explanations.

Evolution and Irreducible Complexity

THEN THERE'S the question of later biological origins. That is, once the first living organism was on the scene, how did all the other life forms we find around us emerge?

The standard explanation I was taught is that it all evolved blindly, one tiny accidental variation at a time, over billions of years. This is the theory of evolution by natural selection, first propounded by Charles Darwin and Alfred Russel Wallace some 160 years ago, and expanded to include modern genetics in the next century.

The implications of this theory were plain to me. Humans were not the culmination of a meaningful plan. We were not here for a purpose. The universe just burped us up. Any meaning we found in life we would have to manufacture ourselves.

What I didn't know at the time was that there was a great deal of misinformation about evolution taught to me, and a lot of important missing information. For example, no one ever bothered to mention that Wallace, the co-discoverer with Darwin of the theory of evolution by accidental variation and natural selection, went on to insist that some sort of creative intelligence must have been involved. For Wallace, a blind evolutionary process of accidental variations and natural selection was insufficient to turn ape-like creatures into human beings, with our unique capacities for speech, reason, and art.[6] He wasn't a Christian or Bible believer, so clearly he wasn't attempting to shoehorn the science into some particular reading of the book of Genesis.[7] Instead, he appears to have been driven to his conclusion purely by an examination of the scientific evidence.

Another thing none of my textbooks mentioned was the truth about nineteenth-century German zoologist Ernst Haeckel's classic embryo drawings. Intended to prove that humans descended from fish-like ancestors, Haeckel's embryo drawings were long a staple of high school biology and college textbooks. They have been used in one form or another for close to 150 years. But it turns out that his drawings were inaccurate[8]—even fraudulent.[9] This was known when I was in high school and college, but the fact was ignored. There is finally some work being done to correct the matter,[10] but it remains to be seen how long it will take textbooks to fully incorporate the truth.

Why has it proven so difficult to reform science education in a case like this, where the error is so obvious? Modern versions of Darwin's theory of evolution form the reigning paradigm for explaining how all the various species emerged in the history of life. And anything that seems to challenge that paradigm faces resistance. However, the good news is that ranking biologists are now open to discussing needed revisions to the theory of evolution. For instance, Dr. Gerd Müller, head of the Department of Theoretical Biology at the University of Vienna, recently observed that emerging findings from various fields of science demand dramatic alterations to the theory.[11]

There are other accomplished scientists who are willing to go even further. Over twenty years ago I happened to catch a science debate on PBS. I was amazed as I heard capable and credentialed scientists challenge the traditional evolutionary story, not on the basis of the Bible or religious arguments, but on the basis of the scientific evidence. One scientist in particular cited evidence from molecular biology that challenged the traditional evolutionary narrative and, as he argued, provided support for the role of intelligent planning and purpose in the origin of living organisms. Later I learned about the bacterial flagellum, a kind of nano-motor with a long whip-like propeller that helps many species of bacteria move through their watery environment. I was fascinated by this marvel of miniaturized technology, with its many interconnected and interdependent parts.[12]

Could the mutation/selection mechanism, or any purely blind, mindless process construct such an engineering marvel? This is explored in Chapter 4. That chapter also explores a more fundamental challenge for modern evolutionary theory: explaining the source of biological variation.

Biology's Big Bang

RESEARCH INTO how life arose involves the study of DNA and molecular machines like the bacterial flagellum, but the fossil record also comes into it, including what is arguably the most astonishing layer of the fossil record, the Cambrian. This ancient stratum testifies to what is known as biology's Big Bang, the relatively sudden appearance of the major groups of animals. What's remarkable is that these animal forms are highly distinct one from another, and they have no precursors below them in the fossil record other than some extremely distantly related sponges and the like. It's as if this menagerie of bizarre sea creatures just popped into existence out of nowhere.

Charles Darwin himself acknowledged what is now known as the "Cambrian Explosion" as a puzzle for his theory 160 years ago, and the mystery remains unresolved today. What do the biology textbooks say about it? The challenge is generally papered over, or ignored altogether. Some scientists speculate that sudden seawater warming during that period expedited the mutation rate, accelerating the evolutionary process. Some say it was the magma outburst through the ocean rifts that brought in huge quantities of nutrients to cause new species to evolve. Others say that an increase in atmospheric oxygen was a big player. Others insist that the sudden explosion of new animal forms is only apparent, an artifact of an incomplete fossil record. However, none of these ideas provide an adequate explanation, and there has been no consensus among scientists.

Some thirty years ago I got a chance to learn more about the Cambrian explosion at a university theater hall event. What I most remember from the talk is the professor discussing Cambrian fossils found in the Yunnan province of China, an extraordinary fossil find that heightened the mystery of the Cambrian explosion.

I feel fortunate that I recently became connected with the marine biologist who gave that talk thirty years ago, Dr. Paul Chien. In Chapter 5, he shares his personal stories of visiting key Cambrian fossil sites, and explains why he has concluded that the best explanation for the Cambrian explosion is not blind evolution but purposeful design.

A Guide for the Perplexed

THIS BOOK is intended as a brief, accessible introduction to what can be a perplexing debate. To that end some of the endnotes include references not only to scholarly works but also to helpful YouTube videos and other resources tailored for people new to the subject. Several of these are also listed on a Recommended Resources page in the back of the book.

Because three terms have proven a particular source of confusion in the origins debate, let's briefly unpack them here.

Materialism—In the context of origins science, materialism refers to the idea that all that exists is matter and energy. In science and philosophy, a materialist is not someone who loves big houses and fast cars. A materialist is someone who claims that everything results from, and can ultimately be explained by, the purely material interactions of energy and particles of matter. There are variations among materialists, and additional nuances we could explore, but for our purposes at this stage, it's enough to keep in view that the worldview known as materialism holds that the workings of matter and energy are sufficient—in and of themselves, without any planning, guidance, or intelligent intervention—to account for the universe, the first life, and all living organisms. The question we pose and seek to explore in this book is whether the latest science actually supports that worldview.

Creationism—In popular culture, including the news media, creationism usually refers to an explicit defense of the creation account found in the first book of the Bible, Genesis. Creationism also typically involves an effort to explain geology and the fossil record in light of the great flood described in Genesis. Creationism defends the Bible as authoritative, and seeks to understand scientific data and discoveries in the context of Scripture. This book is not intended to support or rebut creationism or to defend any scriptural interpretation, but rather to lay out the science as it currently stands. While we do not discuss creationism, however, it is important for the reader to understand what the term typically means and how it differs from both materialism and intelligent design.

Intelligent Design—The theory of intelligent design holds that certain features of the universe and of living things are best explained by an intelligent cause rather than by purely undirected natural processes. In a broader sense, intelligent design is the science of design detection, and it involves recognizing patterns that have been arranged by an intelligent agent for a purpose. The science of design detection crops up in fields as diverse as archaeology, forensics, fraud detection, and physics. Intelligent design may be compatible with one or more religious viewpoints, but it is not itself a religious argument. Intelligent design is restricted to scientific evidence, such as the information content in DNA, the functionally integrated molecular machines in living organisms, or the fine-tuning of the laws and constants of physics and chemistry.

1. THE BIG BANG AND THE FINE-TUNED UNIVERSE

Robert A. Alston

EVER WONDER HOW PHYSICISTS EXPLAIN WHERE THE UNIVERSE came from? For a long time the go-to explanation was that the universe didn't come from anywhere because it simply always existed. But then a funny thing happened. Scientific discoveries revealed that our universe was not always here. It came into existence about 13.8 billion years ago.[1] Sit back while I tell you the story of how we came to this discovery.

Since the invention of the telescope, humans have peered deep into the night sky and seen the wonders of the cosmos previously hidden from us. The more the telescope advanced, the farther we looked and the more we saw. The farther and farther we looked the more it all looked the same: stars and gas clouds. It seemed like it would never end. This reaffirmed the view of many scientists that the universe was infinitely large and infinitely old. At the turn of the twentieth century, this was the conventional wisdom in astronomy.[2]

Then, in 1915, German physicist Albert Einstein changed everything with his general theory of relativity. After working out his calculations (with pencil and paper, I might add), he noticed something odd. The calculations suggested that the universe was either expanding or contracting.[3] This was strange. Einstein thought it had to be a mistake. Like his colleagues at the time, he was certain that the universe was static and eternal. But if it was expanding, it was hardly static, and it was hard to see how an expanding universe could have been expanding forever. So,

Figure 1.1. Albert Einstein.

he did what any good physicist would do. He fiddled with his equation! Einstein scratched into it another number—a "constant"—which would fix his problem, salvaging the static, eternal universe model.

This seemed to solve the problem, but he would later call this change to his equation the "biggest blunder" of his life.

Hubble Trouble

In 1923, at Mt. Wilson Observatory in California, Edwin Hubble was performing the mundane routine of observing nebulae, objects that appeared extended and fuzzy through a telescope, with the largest telescope in the world at that time, and he discovered that some of these were in reality other galaxies. At the same time, this discovery showed that our Milky Way is also a galaxy—not the whole of the observable universe but simply one galaxy among many in the universe.

As if that weren't amazing enough, he noticed a few years later something peculiar about the light emitted from these galaxies. The farther away a galaxy was from us, the more the color of its light was shifted to red. This told him that these galaxies were moving away from us, and that the farther away they were, the faster they were moving away. It appeared as though the universe was expanding, and indeed it was.

When Einstein caught wind of this, he traveled to California to see this phenomenon for himself. What he saw forced him to erase the mathematical addition to his equation and concede that in fact the universe was expanding.

But it wasn't just strange to his way of thinking. The idea of an expanding universe had profound implications. Imagine we are watching the universe on television and can fast-forward and rewind through time like we can with movies at home. What would it look like if we were to rewind and keep rewinding at high speed? If the universe is expanding over time, as Hubble realized, then if we rewound our movie of the universe backwards in time, we would see the universe and all the matter and energy in it shrink into a smaller and smaller space, until eventually the universe shrank down to an infinitesimal point so small that we couldn't see it, and beyond which time as we know it would not exist—a point that physicists call a singularity.

Now imagine that we stop rewinding and press play again. At first we don't see anything on our screen, just blackness. Then, suddenly, out of that infinitesimal point we see a brilliant flash of light as matter and energy pour out, expanding and expanding until we see the universe we recognize today. This brilliant flash, this spark, this flowering of matter and energy at the birth of our universe, has come to be known as the Big Bang.

Georges Lemaître, a Belgian Roman Catholic priest and physicist, was the first to describe a theory similar to what is known today as the Big Bang model.[4] This model points to the universe having a definite beginning. "The evolution of the world can be compared to a display of fireworks that has just ended: some few red wisps, ashes and smoke," Lemaître wrote. "Standing on a cooled cinder, we see the slow fading of the suns, and we try to recall the vanished brilliance of the origin of the worlds."[5]

But this notion that the universe had a beginning did not sit well with many at that time. Some were even disgusted by it. Renowned English astronomer and physicist Arthur Eddington said that "philosophically, the notion of a beginning to the present order of Nature is repugnant."[6] Notice that Eddington didn't claim the science was bad or that these new scientific discoveries were repugnant. Rather, he was bothered by the *philosophical* implications of the discovery.

In fact, it was an opponent of the theory, Sir Fred Hoyle, who coined the name for Lemaître's theory, referring to it mockingly as "this big bang idea" during a radio broadcast.[7] Over the years, many theories were proposed to get rid of this "definite beginning" of the universe, and a war of theories was waged until, finally, in the 1960s, a dramatic discovery left only one winner standing.

Cosmic Static

A PHOTON is a packet of electromagnetic energy. When you turn on a light switch, the light bulb emits an outward flow of light packets, or photons, in the frequency range humans can perceive with their eyes. This allows you to see everything in the room. Other photons exist in frequency ranges invisible to the human eye. But just because you can't see something doesn't mean it isn't there.

On May 20, 1964, at Bell Labs in Holmdel, New Jersey, Robert Wilson and Arno Penzias detected a message from the universe. It came in the form of static noise and it was coming from all directions. They did all they could to remove all possible noise sources, including cleaning off pigeon poop found in the radio antenna. But the noise remained.

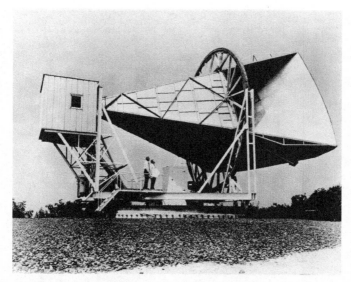

Figure 1.2. The 15-meter Holmdel horn antenna at Bell Labs, used by radio astronomers Robert Wilson and Arno Penzias to discover the Cosmic Microwave Background Radiation.

Penzias later remarked, "It wasn't until we exhausted every possible explanation for the sound's origin that we realized we had stumbled upon something big."[8]

What they discovered were photons permeating the entire universe, photons that had only one possible origin, the Big Bang. These photons are known as the Cosmic Microwave Background Radiation.

Some of you may remember an old TV your grandparents had that displayed static noise on the screen when it wasn't tuned properly to a channel. Perhaps as much as 1% of that noise is the result of photons from the Big Bang.[9] Every cubic centimeter of space has at least 300 of these photons moving through it.[10]

Wilson and Penzias's finding corroborated the Big Bang theory and earned them the Nobel Prize in physics. The background radiation they discovered is believed to be the very photons present shortly after the Big Bang.[11] In the early stages of the universe, its size was only about a

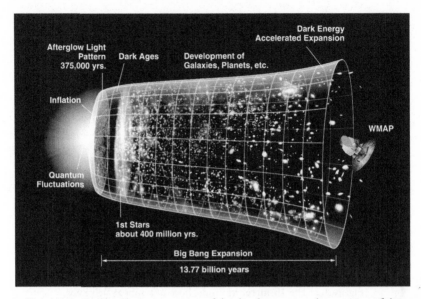

Figure 1.3. Graphical representation of the development and expansion of the universe during its multi-billion-year history. Note the Cosmic Microwave Background Radiation image (Afterglow Light Pattern) represented near the far left of the graphic, shortly after the beginning of the universe.

hundred-millionth the size it is today, and its temperature was extreme, approaching 300 million degrees. Hydrogen couldn't form because electrons and protons quickly broke apart due to the high speed of the collisions. As a result, traveling photons would scatter off the electrons as light scatters in the midst of fog, without dispersing any farther. It took 380,000 years after the Big Bang for the universe to cool enough for hydrogen to form, thus freeing photons to travel in straight lines.

The Cosmic Microwave Background Radiation is a snapshot of the density of photons at that time—a picture of their distribution through the universe after the electrons combined with protons to form hydrogen and the mist was cleared.[12] Sometimes referred to as the Cosmic Rosetta Stone, it has characteristics that give us many clues about the origin and earliest stages of the universe.[13] These photons could only exist in the evenly distributed state we find them in if the universe were once smaller in volume, denser, and thus hotter.[14]

The Big Bang theory won the war of theories and soon became a household name. But there was more to come. Still more evidence supporting the Big Bang theory arrived as our telescopes continued to advance.

A Video Link to the Past

DID YOU know that you have the power to look into the past? No, I don't mean looking at your memories, or at photos of the past. I mean you actually have the power to look at something as it appeared in the past, not in the present.

Look out your window. If you see the sun (please don't look directly at it; I don't want you to harm your eyesight) you aren't seeing the sun as it presently appears, but rather how it looked about eight minutes ago. Or if the moon is up, take a look at it. What you see is not how it presently is but how it was 1.3 seconds ago.

Or next time it's a clear night, see if you can find the brightest star as seen from Earth, Sirius. You are viewing the star not as it is now, but exactly as it was 8.6 years ago.

How is this possible? Although light travels extraordinarily fast, it isn't infinitely fast. It moves at a little over 186,000 miles per second through empty space. That means it takes photons of light from our host star, the sun, just over eight minutes to reach the earth. Sirius is much farther away—about a half a million times farther away—many trillions of miles from Earth, such that its light, as fast as light is, takes fully 8.6 years to reach us.

A light-year is the distance light can travel in one year. This means that if a star precisely 1,000 light-years away exploded (in the common astronomical idiom, "went supernova") precisely 1,000 years ago next week, we'd first witness that spectacular event in the night sky next week.

On a clear night in the countryside, at the right time of year, you can see the Andromeda Galaxy with the naked eye. What looks like a somewhat hazy star is really the central bulge of an entire galaxy, about

2.5 million light years away. What you're seeing when you look at it is essentially a video feed of that galaxy from 2.5 million years ago.

With our massive telescopes we can look even farther into the universe, much farther away than the Andromeda Galaxy, which is the nearest large spiral galaxy to our own. We can view bright celestial objects many billions of light-years away. And the deeper we look into space, the further we look into the past. What we see at the extreme are portions of the universe in their early stages, baby galaxies as they were evolving into their present-day forms. These results also fit well with the Big Bang model.

All of this spells trouble for anyone wanting to keep the idea of a cosmic creator out of the picture. What is known as the Kalam cosmological argument provides part of the reason why.

Kalam

The Kalam cosmological argument, popularized by philosopher William Lane Craig,[15] has two premises and a conclusion:

> Whatever begins to exist has a cause.
>
> The universe began to exist.
>
> Therefore, the universe has a cause.

Is the first premise true? "Whatever begins to exist has a cause." Ask yourself, have you ever seen anything come into existence without a cause? No. And in this case, science and common sense have long agreed—whatever begins to exist does indeed have a cause.

How about the second premise? "The universe began to exist."

We saw above how scientific discoveries have put to rest the idea that the universe is infinitely old. With Einstein's theory of general relativity, the insights and observations provided by Lemaître and Hubble, and the discovery of the Cosmic Microwave Background Radiation, along with other evidence, we can reasonably conclude that the universe began to exist. As leading cosmologist Alexander Vilenkin has stated, "With the proof now in place, cosmologists can no longer hide behind the possibility of a past-eternal universe. There is no escape: they have to face the problem of a cosmic beginning."[16] And Vilenkin, it's worth noting, is not religious and has looked for ways to avoid the theistic implications of the Big Bang. To his credit, he has refused to deny the powerful evidence for a cosmic beginning.

Since the two premises of the Kalam cosmological argument are correct, we can safely draw the conclusion: "Therefore, the universe has a cause."

So, what can we infer about the cause of the universe, about what brought it into being? Remember that when the universe began, the space and time of our universe came into being as well, since those too are part of the fabric of our universe, as demonstrated by Einstein's general theory of relativity. So whatever caused the universe to begin must transcend our universe, existing beyond the limits of the time, matter, and space of our universe. And it must be powerful enough, of course, to cause the entire vast universe to begin.

The cause appears to require another important capacity: the ability to fine-tune.

May the Forces Be with You

HAVE YOU ever gone hiking in a forest? If so, more than likely you found yourself surrounded by a still calmness only trees can bring. Birds were possibly singing and squirrels may have been scurrying about. The forest may have felt so peaceful that it appeared as though nature performed this work easily. But the vastness of life surrounding you was being sustained by physical laws so precisely tuned that if they varied from their current strengths even a little, neither you nor the life surrounding you could exist.

With the birth of our universe some 13.8 billion years ago came not only matter and energy but a remarkable set of laws that govern how everything behaves. So delicately balanced are these laws, constants, and initial conditions that small changes would be catastrophic to life. That is, they seem to be fine-tuned to allow for the existence of life. This realization has reshaped the way scientists view the universe.[17]

The universe is governed by four fundamental forces: gravity, electromagnetism, the strong nuclear force, and the weak nuclear force.[18] From the grandest to the smallest scale, these forces govern the way physical objects behave, and the strength of each one appears to be finely calibrated to allow for the possibility of life in the universe.

For instance, if the fundamental force of gravity were somewhat stronger, stars would burn hotter, emitting far more sterilizing X-ray and gamma-ray photons, rendering the surface of a planet like Earth uninhabitable. The stars would also burn much faster. "Typical stars would burn out in a matter of years, not tens of billions of years," explain cosmologists Geraint Lewis and Luke Barnes, meaning that our sun would burn itself out too quickly, long before life had time to arise and diversify on one of its planets.[19]

What if gravity were somewhat weaker? Stars might not go supernova at all, Lewis and Barnes note, and even if one did "and spilled its material into interstellar space, it would be mainly heavy elements such as silicon and iron, rather than life-supporting oxygen and carbon."[20] No carbon and oxygen, no life.

The electromagnetic force is also fine-tuned. Lewis and Barnes describe a sophisticated calculation by Fred Adams that takes account of the settings of gravity and electromagnetism together. When it's plotted on a two-axis graph, the result is a triangle-shaped zone of stability in a vast sea of joint settings that result in unstable stars. "In this figure," the *Fortunate Universe* authors explain, "the 'stable stars' region takes up less than one part in 10^{35} of the whole plot."[21] In other words, the stable-star settings are one in a trillion times a trillion times a hundred billion. Fortunate indeed.

Or consider the strong nuclear force. "If we nudge the strength of the strong force upwards by just 0.4 percent, stars produce a wealth of carbon, but the route to oxygen is cut off," Lewis and Barnes note. What if we go in the other direction? "Decreasing the strength of the strong force by a similar 0.4 percent has the opposite effect: all carbon is rapidly transformed into oxygen, providing the universe with plenty of water, but leaving it devoid of carbon."[22]

The focus on carbon is not arbitrary or due to an unwillingness to imagine other live possibilities. No other element appears remotely capable of replacing carbon as the central element in the buzz of information-processing activity essential to all life. Due to the cooperation of electromagnetism and the strong nuclear force, precise energy levels exist which allow helium atoms to fuse together to make beryllium-8 and then carbon. If these energy levels didn't coincide, the particles would fly apart before they had time to form carbon.

This finely tuned carbon resonance was predicted by Fred Hoyle, and after his prediction proved correct, he commented, "A common-sense interpretation of the facts suggests that a super-intellect has monkeyed with physics, as well as with chemistry and biology, and that there are no blind forces worth speaking about in nature. The numbers one calculates from the facts seem to me so overwhelming as to put this conclusion almost beyond question."[23] Hoyle wasn't religious, so much so that he long resisted the evidence of a cosmic beginning. It seems apparent then that the scientific evidence led him to make the above remark, not religious belief.

This is just a quick and partial survey of how the fundamental forces of nature are fine-tuned to allow for life in the universe.

A Golf Ball Universe is a Livable Universe

SOMETHING ELSE that had to be fine-tuned to allow for life: the texture of the universe at the Big Bang. Weird but true.

Imagine you are holding a ping pong ball. Pay close attention to the smoothness of the ball. Now imagine you are holding a golf ball with its uneven, dimpled surface. Now finally, imagine you are holding a jagged, unevenly shaped rock. The universe at its inception had a texture akin to the golf ball, rather than to the ping pong ball or the jagged rock. That is, it wasn't extremely smooth like a ping pong ball, or highly uneven like the jagged rock. Instead it was relatively uniform but with some variation, akin to the surface of a dimpled golf ball.

And a good thing it was. Our golf ball universe is like the baby bear's porridge that Goldilocks ate—just right. If the dips in the texture of the early universe had been deep beyond a certain narrow limit, there would be massive pockets of gravity. Galactic structures would have clumped together, leading to a bedlam of collisions and explosions lethal to life. Alternately, if the texture of the universe were smooth like a ping pong ball, there would have been too little gravitational pull to form galaxies and planets quickly enough, and thus again, no life. And the margin for error is extremely tight. For life to be possible in the universe, the degree of uniformity—not too much, not too little—had to be fine-tuned within a very narrow range.[24]

The Best Drink in the Universe

LET'S BRING the fine-tuning discussion closer to home. Water. Most of your body is water. Most of Earth's surface is covered by water. Water may seem ordinary to you, but it's actually one of the most extraordinary compounds in the universe, and its suite of unusual properties are essential for life. It's a story of extraordinary fine-tuning for life. Noted author and biochemist Michael Denton ably summarizes the many ways it is uniquely suited for life:

> This wonder fluid is fit for life on Earth in an absolutely stunning number of ways. It is fit for the formation of proto-planetary discs, for the formation of the planets, for the formation of the oceans, and for their subsequent preservation.
>
> Water is uniquely fit for the hydrological cycle, the tectonic cycle, and the temperature regulation of the human body. The properties of water play a critical part in the formation of the great oceanic currents, which circulate crucial nutrients throughout the world ocean. Those

currents play a key role in global temperature regulation and modera-
tion and in controlling the CO_2 levels in the atmosphere.

Water is superbly and uniquely fit to dissolve the minerals in the
rocks, and her great solvation powers are fit for the circulation of nutrients both in the blood stream and in the oceans. Water's expansion on
freezing and its other unique thermal properties preserve large bodies
of water in the higher latitudes.

Water is fit for bioenergetics by providing the proton flows that
play such a unique and critical role in the generation of cellular energy.
Water's transparency to light is fit for photosynthesis. Water is not
only the giver of oxygen, but also uniquely fit for its use in human res-
piration.[25]

Now, someone might say, well fine, but water was inevitable, wasn't
it? With all the different elementary particles in the period after the Big
Bang combining in so many different ways, weren't we bound to get a
compound like water, even if the laws and constants of the universe were
somewhat different? No, actually not. Again, if you think about the
fundamental forces of nature, if you tweak some of them even a little,
you don't get oxygen. You don't even get elements heavier than hydrogen
and helium outside of stars without several things being just so. And
you can't get anything remotely like water from elements as simple as
hydrogen and helium. Additionally, even if a universe with slightly different strengths for its fundamental forces still managed to produce a
version of H_2O, how might it be crucially altered if the strong or weak
nuclear force, or electromagnetic force, differed slightly? One or more of
water's unique, life-essential properties likely would be altered, spoiling
the recipe for life.

Fine-Tuning +

ONE COULD easily fill a whole book with examples of how our universe is
fine-tuned to allow for life. There are books out there that do just this.[26]
What you have above is just the briefest sampling. But even this quick
fly-by urges the question: What caused the universe to be fine-tuned in
this way?

If you were a space explorer and, after landing on Mars, discovered a tunnel to an underground room with a climate control system with dozens of sliding knobs, and each one was set at just the right position to allow you to live for days at a time in the room—right temperature setting, right mix of gases in the air, right air pressure, etc.—you would reasonably conclude that the knobs had been purposefully fine-tuned for creatures like you. The laws and constants of the universe are fine-tuned to a far greater degree than this to allow for life.

Now, that fine-tuning isn't by itself enough to make life possible, any more than the hypothetical underground room on Mars was enough by itself. Besides the many finely tuned parameters of the universe, life also requires a host of other fine-tuning parameters that we find fulfilled in our particular location in the universe, planet Earth. Such multi-layered fine-tuning suggests planning and purpose. As the late, great Princeton theoretical physicist Freeman Dyson said, "The more I examine the universe and study the details of its architecture, the more evidence I find that the universe in some sense must have known that we were coming."[27]

A Multiverse Mess

There are many other well-established examples of fine-tuning,[28] which are widely accepted, including by researchers who oppose intelligent design. From what we have covered in this chapter alone—gravity balanced on a razor's edge, the delicate relationship between electromagnetism and the strong nuclear force, the texture of the universe at the Big Bang, and the amazing properties of water—we see that the parameters required for life in the universe are highly improbable. Yet despite the evidence for planning and purpose, some people still argue that we are here by accident, never mind the long odds.

If faced with a situation in which the probability of success was not in your favor, what would you do to ensure success? How would you raise the probability to be in your favor? When faced with the reality of the fine-tuned parameters of our universe, together with a remarkable planet hospitable to life, some scientists have tried to change the equation by proposing that our universe and our hospitable home were essentially inevitable. They do this by proposing the existence of multiple universes, or what is often called the "multiverse."

The multiverse hypothesis proposes that there are many universes outside our own, each one tuned differently. So, for instance, in one the strength of gravity might be ten times greater than it is in ours; in another, gravity might be much weaker. And on and on with the various other parameters. Then, it is argued, if the number of these universes is astronomically high, perhaps even infinite, then the probability of at least one universe existing with all the right parameters for life is likely, and we just happen to be lucky enough to be in it.[29] Indeed, we should expect ourselves to be in such a universe; otherwise we wouldn't be around to notice our good fortune. Somehow, a group of scientists have managed to flip the low-probability, fine-tuned universe into a highly probable universe. Or have they?

The first thing to note is that there is no testable, empirical evidence that any of these other universes actually exist. Even if these multiple universes did exist, how would we ever know? There is no known way of determining if these universes even exist, since we are limited to observing what is in our known universe. Thus, the multiverse is little more than a hypothetical idea. One influential theoretical physicist compared the idea of other universes with different constants to leprechauns and unicorns.[30]

In addition, one must consider what is creating this massive number of universes. There would have to be some sort of universe-generating mechanism. The most common notion of the multiverse is called the Landscape Multiverse, based on a combination of string theory and eternal inflation.[31] The Landscape Multiverse suggests that there are infinitely many island universes arising from some sort of universe-generating landscape, each universe island containing different higher-level physical laws and constants.[32] The only problem is that this "universe-generating landscape" itself requires fine tuning.[33] In an attempt to remove the fine-tuning problem, they have merely moved it from our observable universe to an unobservable, hypothetical multiverse.

In "A Brief History of the Multiverse" physicist Paul Davies observed the following concerning the multiverse hypothesis:

> How seriously can we take this explanation for the friendliness of nature? Not very, I think. For a start, how is the existence of the other universes to be tested? To be sure, all cosmologists accept that there are some regions of the universe that lie beyond the reach of our telescopes, but somewhere on the slippery slope between that and the idea that there are an infinite number of universes, credibility reaches a limit. As one slips down that slope, more and more must be accepted on faith, and less and less is open to scientific verification.
>
> Extreme multiverse explanations are therefore reminiscent of theological discussions. Indeed, invoking an infinity of unseen universes to explain the unusual features of the one we do see is just as *ad hoc* as invoking an unseen Creator. The multiverse theory may be dressed up in scientific language, but in essence it requires the same leap of faith.[34]

Davies is partly right, but partly wrong, I would argue. The multiverse hypothesis is indeed *ad hoc*, a leap of faith untethered from observational evidence. But what of the alternative hypothesis—a designer and maker of the matter, energy, space, time, and finely tuned laws of our universe? Our uniform experience shows us only one type of cause with the demonstrated power to purposefully tailor and arrange parts in a sophisticated fashion—intelligent agency. We see minds doing this all the time, producing software codes and cars, planes, drones, and satellites, coffee makers and calculators; on and on the list could go. And we never find other types of causes doing so. The fine-tuning of the universe at the Big Bang is such an example of parts tailored and arranged to fulfill a purpose. Inferring a creative intelligence for the fine-tuning of the universe, then, is not *ad hoc*. It is an inference to the best explanation, a tried and true mode of reasoning in the historical sciences.

Review: Your Turn

1. Why did Einstein change his equation?
2. Why did he eventually call it the biggest blunder of his life?
3. Who was Edwin Hubble, and what did he discover at the Mt. Wilson Observatory in California?
4. What might happen if gravity were a little stronger than it is? If it were a little weaker?
5. Why do scientists think the universe is fine-tuned to support life?
6. The space, time, matter, and energy of our fine-tuned universe had a beginning. Something caused the universe to come into being. What are some of the characteristics we can infer about the cause for this cosmic creation event?
7. How is the idea of the multiverse used to explain fine-tuning? What problems, if any, are there with the multiverse explanation?

2. INFORMATION AND THE ORIGIN OF LIFE

Eric H. Anderson

W<small>E SAW IN THE LAST CHAPTER HOW A SERIES OF SCIENTIFIC DIS-</small>coveries in the twentieth century broke strongly against the idea of an eternal universe. Our cosmos had a beginning. And at some point life here on earth had a beginning. How did it happen? Is there any reason to think it was planned and purposeful, or was it just sheer coincidence—the lucky result of some cosmic lottery?

In the final episode of *Star Trek: The Next Generation*, the immortal and nearly omnipotent Q gives Captain Picard the unique opportunity of witnessing the origin of life on Earth. Picard suddenly finds himself standing in a chaotic landscape filled with lava flows and volcanoes that dot the scene. Earth is dark and ominous and utterly devoid of life. As Picard gathers himself from the sudden leap through time and takes stock of his surroundings, Q points excitedly to an oily puddle of chemicals near a volcanic vent.[1]

"Come here," Q says. "There's something I want to show you. You see this? This is you."

Picard gives Q a skeptical glance.

"I'm serious! Right here," insists Q, gazing intently at the chemical sludge. "Life is about to form on this planet for the very first time. A group of amino acids are about to combine to form the first protein—the building blocks of what you call life."

Then, with a playful sneer about the insignificance of humankind, Q says, "Strange, isn't it? Everything you know, your entire civilization, it all begins right here in this little pond of goo."

This memorable exchange between the time-traveling Q and the captain of the Enterprise is of course a work of fiction. But it more or less accurately reflects an idea found in current college textbooks and scientific articles. The idea is this: *If conditions are just right, non-living molecules can give rise to the building blocks of life and, eventually, to life itself. And at some point on the early Earth, the conditions were just right, and voila! It happened. Then, from that first simple life form evolved all the life we now find on Earth, including us. We are the descendants of that first humble organism in that long-ago chemical soup.*

But does the idea hold up to scrutiny? What does the most current evidence suggest for this "goo-to-you" scenario?

Here we are focused on the first part of that story. That is, the claim on the table is that life first emerged through purely natural processes, without any intelligent guidance, intervention, or creative act. The claim is that non-living molecules, by themselves, through nothing more than the laws of physics and chemistry and the random distribution of molecules and chemical reactions, came together to form the building blocks of life, and eventually life itself. This is an idea known as *abiogenesis*.

It's a scientific claim in the sense that we can subject it to scrutiny, testing, and analysis. Of course, we can't travel back in time like Q and Captain Picard to witness the origin of life on Earth. So we can never verify via direct observation the claim that through purely natural processes non-living chemicals turned into organic chemicals and eventually into a living organism on the early Earth. But notice that our ability to investigate any claim about distant historical events is limited in this way, whether it be origin-of-life (OOL) studies, paleontology, archeology, or forensics. Instead, we examine the claim in light of the knowledge and experience we do have, and infer past causes from present clues. In the case of the origin of life, investigators can try to recreate early Earth conditions in the lab. We can run through numerous scenarios with different chemical constituents. We can use our knowledge of chemistry and physics to determine what kinds of reactions would actually be required to produce something like Q's "first protein." We can observe the minimal requirements for the simplest self-reproducing organism alive today and make educated assessments about whether simpler forms of life are possible. We can analyze the many challenges facing a purely natural origin of life and draw reasonable conclusions about whether it is likely to be true.

Assumption Alert

BEFORE WE examine the science, there is one thing we need to be aware of. In addition to the scientific idea of abiogenesis and whatever evidence is marshalled in favor of it, there is an idea or assumption that often hides behind the abiogenesis claim. Here it is in a nutshell: *Even if our current understanding of the origin of life is inaccurate and incomplete, some kind of purely natural process must have generated the first life. Even before we look at the evidence, this must be true. The only question is precisely what that natural process was.*

It is crucial to be aware of this working assumption lurking in the background, to be able to spot it when it hides in the shadows, and to recognize it for what it is. If we want to reason through the question of whether life arose blindly, without intelligent guidance, if we want to see what the physical evidence may be trying to tell us, then we need to set aside this assumption. To cling to the assumption while also looking to investigate the question of whether life first arose through purely natural, unguided processes is akin to trying to investigate whether a house fire was arson or not, but then refusing to consider the possibility that it was arson.

The point may seem so obvious as to be almost unnecessary to make, but many origin-of-life scientists do insist on considering only unguided natural causes for the origin of the first life and, when challenged with contrary evidence, insist that they won't consider anything other

Figure 2.1. Artist's conception of a primordial landscape with cometary bombardment and a pre-biotic chemical soup in the foreground.

than purely natural causes because supposedly that wouldn't be science. While they insist that they are simply following the evidence, no holds barred, in fact they are barring a possible explanation before they even consider the evidence.

Better to ask ourselves, what does the evidence suggest? Not selective facts chosen to prop up a philosophical position, but the broad array of evidence across the board, the latest and best science we have on the subject, analyzed as carefully and as objectively as we can. What does that kind of careful, objective science say about the origin of life?

Spontaneous Life?

Early philosophers and observers of nature, from the Babylonians, to the great Chinese and Indian civilizations, to the ancient Greeks, contemplated the origin of living organisms. How is it that maggots seemed to spontaneously appear in a corpse, or worms from the muddy bank of a river, or even mice from a barrel of wheat? Lacking powerful microscopes and other sophisticated detection equipment, and also lacking

2. Information and the Origin of Life   / **41**

in many cases the strong tradition of experiment-based science we take for granted today, early observers could only guess. It seemed as if those creatures arose spontaneously.

It wasn't completely crazy. Some simple observations even seemed to support the idea: get the right conditions, such as the corpse or the mud or the grain, add in the right weather and temperature and, sure enough, over time you were bound to observe maggots and worms and mice. It was an easy mental leap from this observation to the conclusion that such creatures arose spontaneously under the right conditions. As a result, for centuries this idea of spontaneous generation was accepted as the answer to the origin of many forms of life.

Even after the invention of the microscope the idea lived on, but its days were numbered.

Though not the only critic, the great French microbiologist Louis Pasteur (1822–1895) is often credited with the careful experimental approach that finally delivered the death blow to the idea of spontaneous generation. At a time when many scientists still accepted the idea of spontaneous generation, Pasteur performed several experiments with sterilized containers and liquids demonstrating that, when these experiments were carefully performed, living organisms did not arise. Pasteur was later quoted as saying, "Never will the doctrine of spontaneous generation recover from the mortal blow of this simple experiment. There is no known circumstance in which it can be confirmed that microscopic beings came into the world… without parents similar to themselves."[2]

Maxime Schwartz offered the following reflection in the *Journal of Applied Microbiology* on Pasteur's experiments:

> By extremely painstaking experimental methodology, he demonstrated that the appearance of micro-organisms in a presterilized medium could always be explained by germs coming from the outside. He thus succeeded in discrediting any experimental basis for the theory of spontaneous generation.

On a philosophical level, the repercussions were resounding. The onset of life was decidedly not a predictable phenomenon, regularly occurring in any fermentable medium. The question of the origin of life was thereafter clearly set forth—and remains so today.[3]

In other words, if, as Pasteur showed, living organisms normally only come from other living organisms, where then did the *first* organism come from?

A Rose by Another Name

Looking back, we might be tempted to think that our forebears were simple-minded and foolish. How could they believe in spontaneous generation for so many centuries? After all, every small child today knows that mice don't just arise from wheat, or worms from mud, or maggots from rotting meat. Instead, these creatures come from parent organisms like themselves. We are understandably proud of the great scientific progress that has been made, particularly over the past few hundred years, and we can scarcely comprehend how anyone could not understand what we now take for granted.

Yet if we step away from specific examples like maggots and worms and mice and look at the underlying principle of spontaneous generation more broadly, we are forced to admit that a little more humility is in order. Just as our forebears were wrong about spontaneous generation, is it possible that today's claims of abiogenesis are also in need of careful scrutiny?

Of course, abiogenesis proponents today do not believe in spontaneous generation as it was understood long ago. Yet although the idea of life arising from non-life has been thoroughly discredited by Pasteur and other researchers with respect to the living organisms we observe around us today, what about the beginning of life, what about the first organism? Even if life can't spontaneously arise easily and often, perhaps it could happen at least once, under even more special conditions? The modern abiogenesis story pushes the formation of life from non-life back to a remarkably lucky one-time event in the remote past, yet the core principle remains: *if conditions are just right, non-living matter can turn into living organisms.*

Enter Darwin's Warm Little Pond

IN 1859, just five years before Louis Pasteur rejected the idea of spontaneous generation at a scientific conference, another European, Charles Darwin, published his formidable work that would become a landmark in biology, *On the Origin of Species.*

Darwin's book did not attempt to address the origin of life. He simply assumed one or more original self-reproducing organisms, and built his theory of evolution from there. Beginning in later editions he does mention "the Creator" as the possible source of the first living organism or organisms, but he apparently held out hope for a purely naturalistic source for the origin of the first life. For even after Pasteur proved that spontaneous generation wasn't happening all around us, Darwin privately offered an explanation for the origin of life that didn't involve a creator.

"How on earth is the absence of all living things in Pasteur's experiment to be accounted for?" Darwin asked his friend Joseph Hooker in an 1871 letter. Darwin went on from there to speculate: "It is often said that all the conditions for the first production of a living organism are now present, which could ever have been present.— But if (& oh what a big if) we could conceive in some warm little pond with all sorts of ammonia & phosphoric salts,—light, heat, electricity &c present, that a protein compound was chemically formed, ready to undergo still more complex changes..."[4]

Darwin immediately acknowledged that in the present natural environment such a "protein compound" would be "instantly devoured, or absorbed." But perhaps it wasn't always this way? Perhaps before living things were around, he mused, before life had formed on the early Earth, a protein compound could have survived and continued to evolve—undergoing, as Darwin suggested, "still more complex changes."

Notice that Darwin wasn't proposing that life can easily arise from non-living matter, or that the process often occurs. Rather, he was asking, what if, perhaps under just the right conditions, an early precursor to life could arise from non-living chemicals? And if so, might not that precursor eventually lead to a living organism?

Darwin was not alone in his musings about the possibility of chemicals coming together in a blind shuffle to form a living organism. In the decades that followed, a tremendous amount of effort would be spent trying to flesh out the idea and provide some experimental support.

Chemical Soup, Anyone?

In the early 1920s, the great Russian biochemist Alexander Oparin proposed that life originated on Earth through a series of biochemical steps. Oparin thought that simple organic molecules could form on the early Earth in an atmosphere containing methane, ammonia, hydrogen, and water vapor, but one in which, unlike our present atmosphere, oxygen was absent or significantly minimized, preventing oxidation of other chemicals in the environment. (Such an oxygen-starved atmosphere is known as a reducing atmosphere.) Oparin speculated that after these simple organic molecules had formed under such conditions, occasionally they would react to form more complex molecules, developing new properties and eventually turning into a living organism.[5]

Shortly thereafter, British geneticist J. B. S. Haldane proposed that the primitive ocean on the early Earth was like a "hot dilute soup" in which simple organic compounds could have formed.[6] Like Oparin, and Darwin before, Haldane thought the simple compounds would react with others, forming more complex compounds, then the components of living cells, and eventually a living organism.

Although their ideas were initially dismissed by many scientists, Oparin's and Haldane's suggestions that life started on Earth through a kind of "chemical evolution" gained traction. Some scientists remained skeptical, but to many it seemed that it was only a matter of time before the case was clinched for this scenario. After all, if Darwin had shown that all the wonderful complexity and diversity of life forms on our planet could evolve from that first simple organism, through a process of natural selection acting on random variations without the need for any guiding intelligence, then perhaps that first living organism also could be explained as the result of a purely natural process. Perhaps nature itself was the creator—producing from the simplest chemical elements the building blocks of life and, eventually, life itself.

This possibility continued to tantalize the biochemists of the day. Yet while the theory sounded good, what was still needed was hard experimental evidence. Enter Stanley Miller and Harold Urey.

A Personal Journey

WHEN I first learned about the famous experiments performed by Stanley Miller and Harold Urey at the University of Chicago,[7] I was impressed as I heard about the formation of amino acids from nothing but simple compounds and a bit of electricity—amino acids that, I was told by abiogenesis proponents, could have come together to form simple proteins and eventually more complex organic molecules, and eventually life, just as Q told Captain Picard and just as Darwin speculated.

Was it true? Rather than just accepting what I was being told, I decided to find out for myself. As I read more about the origin of life and the often heated debate over the possibility of undirected chemical reactions producing a primitive living organism, I wondered why there was still so much debate if Miller and Urey had shown that life, or at least the building blocks of life, could arise from a purely natural process.

After all, the preeminent scientist George Gaylord Simpson had noted fully sixty years ago that "at a recent meeting in Chicago, a highly distinguished international panel of experts was polled. All considered the experimental production of life in the laboratory imminent."[8] So, if nearly 70 years ago, Miller and Urey had made such a big breakthrough, and if at the turn of the next decade, in 1960, a distinguished panel of

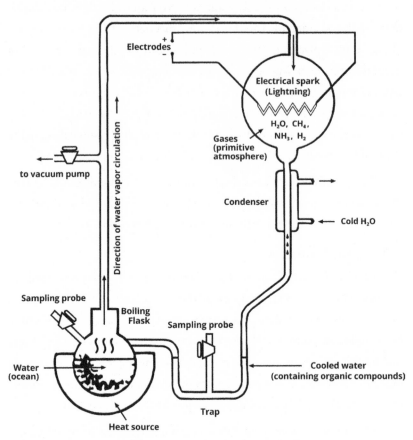

Figure 2.2. Rendering of the setup used in the famous Miller-Urey experiments.

experts confidently affirmed that laboratory confirmation for the purely natural origin of life was just around the corner, what was there still to debate all these decades later?

I wondered if perhaps the debate raged on because some people believed that a naturalistic origins story would conflict with their personal religious or philosophical views about a purposeful creation. Maybe the researchers had sealed the deal decades ago, and the religious folks just weren't willing to face the music. Yet as I researched the topic, I found that many of the scientists and authors who were critical of the Miller-Urey experiment raised questions based not on any religious viewpoint, but on the science. Indeed, one of them, Dean Kenyon, had been a leading proponent of a naturalistic origin of life, and had literally written the book on the topic—or to be precise, had co-authored a leading origin-of-life textbook, *Biochemical Predestination*.[9]

I myself didn't have a philosophical or religious concern with the abiogenesis story, but something about it smelled fishy. And the more I researched it, the fishier it smelled.

To be sure, Miller and Urey had done wonderful science and created a very ingenious experiment. They were at the forefront of research in the early 1950s. Through their hard work and dedicated efforts, we learned new and important things about how non-living chemicals behave and how certain organic compounds might be formed. But as I investigated further, what I found was this: the idea that the now-iconic Miller-Urey experiment placed us firmly on the path to explaining a purely natural origin of life—an idea pushed primarily, I might add, by people other than Miller and Urey—is simply false.

In the decades since, nearly every aspect of the Miller-Urey experiment has been challenged. It taught us interesting things, but it fell far short of replicating a mindless chemical evolutionary process or the relevant conditions likely to have held sway on the early Earth. From the reducing atmosphere used in the experiment,[10] to the need for just the right amount of energy,[11] to the careful isolation of the tender chemicals from unfavorable interfering cross-reactions,[12] to the protective environment in which the reactions took place, careful observers have questioned the relevance of the Miller-Urey results to the origin of life on the early Earth.[13] Yet the Miller-Urey experiment is still touted in many high school and college textbooks as proof that the formation of the chemicals necessary for life on the early Earth is no longer a serious problem and has been largely solved.[14] Nothing could be further from the truth.

And that isn't even half the problem for abiogenesis.

Flash in a Flask

EVEN IF we were to accept the inaccurate textbook story of the Miller-Urey experiment as gospel, we would not be justified in concluding that it showed a viable pathway to a naturalistic origin of life. That's because, at the end of their carefully controlled, intelligently designed and intelligently guided experiment, they were still light years away from getting a simple living organism.

There are so many additional problems with the overall abiogenesis story that it is hard to know where to begin. Researchers have identified more than a dozen serious problems with the abiogenesis account. Most of them, even individually by themselves, doom the abiogenesis idea. When taken together, they constitute a devastating critique of the naturalistic origin-of-life story. In 1982, organic chemist and molecular biologist A. G. Cairns-Smith raised several objections against the typical "origin of life" simulation experiments.[15] Soon thereafter, chemist Charles Thaxton, geochemist Roger Olsen, and materials scientist Walter Bradley provided a rigorous critique of the many origin-of-life proposals and speculations. They referred to a "crisis in the chemistry of origins" and observed that "the undirected flow of energy through a primordial atmosphere and ocean is at present a woefully inadequate explanation for the incredible complexity associated with even simple living systems, and is probably wrong." They go on to conclude that "reasonable doubt exists whether simple chemicals on a primitive earth did spontaneously evolve (or organize themselves) into the first life."[16]

The situation has not improved since that time. Quite the contrary. Each additional avenue of research seems to spawn additional questions and challenges to the abiogenesis story. Researchers' abiogenesis ideas are regularly shot down by other origin-of-life researchers, who then go on to propose their own, equally inadequate suggestions.

A recent 2019 paper examines multiple proposed locations for the origin of life, including Darwin's "warm little pond," hot springs, outer space, and (a popular suggestion nowadays) deep-sea hydrothermal vents. The researchers conclude that none of these locations are able to meet the requirements for abiogenesis, and instead propose a geyser system "driven by a natural nuclear reactor."[17] In a recent review article on origin-of-life research, astrobiologist and theoretical physicist Sara Walker lauds the efforts that have been made in origin-of-life research to date, but acknowledges that "we have not yet been able to answer the question of how life first emerged."

Walker appears unwavering in her faith that the first life on earth arose naturalistically, but after examining problems with many current attempts to address the origin of life, she concludes that "novel approaches... may be required" and hopes for a "new theory of physics" that can help bridge the gap. Walker comments that the task of understanding how life arose from purely natural causes might be as difficult as "unifying general relativity and quantum theory," and suggests that solving the puzzle of our origins might occur only "if we are so lucky as to stumble on [a] new fundamental understanding of life."[18]

Thus have the days of early excitement over the Miller-Urey experiment been replaced by an understanding of a most sobering reality. In the remainder of this chapter and in the next, we will review just two of the key problems with the modern abiogenesis story: the need for biological information and the challenge of self-replication.

More Information, Please

THE EARLY 1980s were a time of great excitement in the computer world. Just a few years earlier Apple Computer Company had been founded by Steve Jobs, Steve Wozniak, and Ronald Wayne, kicking off a revolution of affordable personal computers that began making their way into the hands of hobbyists, computer clubs, and a few early homes. Apple's popularity had exploded with the introduction of the Apple II in 1977. Several other manufacturers also had started developing and selling computers directly to consumers, with names like Altair, Texas Instruments, TRS-80, Sinclair, Atari, Commodore, and others.

My father was an engineer by training and had more than a passing interest in the young field of personal computing. As soon as circumstances and the family budget allowed, he loaded my three brothers and me into the car early one Saturday morning for an eight-hour drive to a computer fair where we pored over the thrilling new offerings in this young field. Ignoring our exhaustion from a busy day, we talked excitedly the whole drive home about the new technology we had seen.

Although my father was a frugal man, he had done his research and was determined to spend his hard-earned funds on a quality machine that could be used for years to come. After careful analysis of the pros and cons and the costs and benefits of various systems, at a level of detail that only an engineer could appreciate, he settled on one of the better Apple II-compatible systems he could find at the time. With my mother's eventual agreement that this would take the place of all our gifts that Christmas, he reached deep into his pocketbook and placed the order.

Looking back, I have to smile at our first computer, one that cost more than many high-end gaming systems today. When we finally got our new computer a few weeks later on Christmas Eve, we could scarcely wait until Christmas morning to set it up. It had all the bells and whistles! A whopping 64K of RAM (not the 48K that most of the Apple IIs came with at the time), a 5.25" floppy disk drive, five video games, ten blank floppy disks, a simple joystick, and, best of all, a large CRT *color* monitor! (No way we were going to settle for a monochrome green monitor!)

Within a few months, we added a dot matrix printer and a second drive. Now we had two—count 'em, two!—5.25" floppy disk drives, which enabled the computer to run more advanced word processing programs and also allowed us to copy disks much more easily.

Although our family did not even own a television, we were soon the technological envy of our friends and acquaintances. We had the first personal computer of anyone in the neighborhood. Suddenly our garage, which had earlier been converted into a family play area, became the scene of countless weekends and late nights as my siblings and I and our friends huddled around that low-resolution color monitor playing exciting round after round of early 8-bit computer games. To my parents' chagrin, my sleeping habits took a serious turn for the worse as the afternoons at the computer turned into evenings, then nights, then early mornings.

But it wasn't all games. My father's engineering background instilled in us a desire to not just use the technology, but to understand how things worked.

I purchased an early manual on the Apple operating system and studied the details for hours. I learned how to "hack" into computer games and change some of the game parameters and screen displays. Not a particularly valuable thing in its own right, but in the process I learned valuable lessons about file systems, disk sectors, storage protocols, and other inner workings of the computer.

I also taught myself to program in BASIC, the simple integer language used by the Apple II, and began to write my own programs, eventually doing some early database work. Soon I delved into COBOL and Fortran, and even spent a couple of summers helping program an old Burroughs computer in Hexadecimal—now that was tedious work! Eventually I took to building my own computers.

Looking back on this formative time, both in the computer industry and in my own life, I am grateful for the opportunity I had, in my own small way in my own small corner of the world, to witness firsthand and up close and personal the remarkable transformation that computers and information technology would come to play in the world. Perhaps the biggest takeaway from the experience was the realization that information was key. It wasn't the metal or the plastic or the wires or the magnetic disks. Yes, those were important. But it was the information, both in the subtle way the physical parts were arranged for a particular purpose, and more obviously in the way the codes and the programs brought those careful arrangements of parts to life. It was always the same thing at the heart of every game, every database, every floppy disk sector, every function: information.

In the world of complex functional systems, information is king. What does that have to do with the origin of life? As it turns out, an important form of digital information was around long before computers. Information sits—or rather hums and dances—at the heart of all life.

A Strand of DNA Walks into a Bar...

THE STORY is well known in scientific circles, almost the stuff of legend. One Saturday in February 1953, English scientist Francis Crick walked into *The Eagle* pub in Cambridge, England, with his American research partner James Watson, and announced that the two "had discovered the secret of life!"[19]

Watson and Crick might be forgiven for their bravado. After all, they had, along with important assistance from Rosalind Franklin and Maurice Wilkins, discovered the structure of the large organic molecule arguably most central to life: deoxyribonucleic acid (DNA).

Determining the three-dimensional helical structure of this important molecule was achievement enough, but it also occurred to Watson and Crick that the pairing of nucleotides across the twisting ladder of DNA suggested "a possible copying mechanism for the genetic material."[20] That is, the structure of DNA might facilitate the copying of genetic information from generation to generation. They turned out to be spectacularly correct.

A remarkable glimpse into history has been preserved in the form of a handwritten letter Crick penned to his 12-year old son, Michael, on March 19, 1953.[21] Despite writing to a young man not yet in his teens, Crick lays out the structure of DNA in some detail:

> My Dear Michael,
>
> Jim Watson and I have probably made a most important discovery. We have built a model for the structure of de-oxy-ribose-nucleic-acid (read it carefully) called D.N.A. for short....

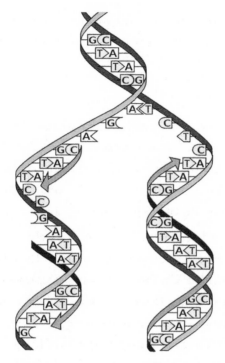

Figure 2.3. DNA structure, showing the nucleotide base pairs
adenine and thymine (A/T) and cytosine and guanine (C/G), and
the double helix unwinding as part of the copying process.

Now on one chain, as far as we can see, one can have the bases in
any order, but if their order is fixed, then the order on the other chain
is also fixed. For example, suppose the first chain goes A-T-C-A-G-T-T,
then the second must go T-A-G-T-C-A-A.

Crick went on to suggest that this complementary pairing of the two
DNA strands not only shed light on the information-bearing properties
of DNA and the existence of what would later become known as the
"genetic code," but also hinted at a potential copying mechanism:

> It is like a code. If you are given one set of letters you can write down
> the others.

> Now we believe that the D.N.A. is a code. That is, the order of the
> bases (the letters) makes one gene different from another gene (just as
> one page of print is different from another)....

In other words we think we have found the basic copying mechanism by which life comes from life.... You can understand that we are very excited. We have to have a letter off to *Nature* in a day or so. Read this carefully so that you understand it. When you come home we will show you the model.

As I ponder Crick's letter and imagine what it must have been like for Crick and Watson to discover the structure of DNA, I am impressed by their insight into the implications as they recognized not only the structure of DNA but also the existence of a code, the key role of information, and the way "life comes from life," as Crick explained to his son.

Just a few years later, in 1957, Crick gave a lecture in which he outlined what he called the "sequence hypothesis."[22] The following year he published a paper titled "On Protein Synthesis."[23] Among other details, he proposed that the "specificity" of a piece of DNA (meaning, in essence, the information contained in that piece of DNA) results from the sequence or the ordering of the base molecules or bases. In other words, it isn't merely the physical structure or the chemical makeup of the DNA bases that store information, but the arrangement of those bases.

Like the letters of the English alphabet you are reading in this book, it is the *order* of the letters that conveys the information, not the color of the ink or the type of paper used.

At least in this regard, Crick's sequence hypothesis was spot on. Watson and Crick's work stands as a singular achievement in the history of science. "Watson and Crick's discovery would forever change our understanding of the nature of life," observed philosopher of science Stephen Meyer. "At the close of the nineteenth century, most biologists thought life consisted solely of matter and energy. But after Watson and Crick, biologists came to recognize the importance of a third fundamental entity in living things: information."[24]

The Language of Life

Since that fateful day in the English pub in 1953, the problem of explaining the origin of life has increasingly been recognized as a problem of explaining the origin of biological information. Where did the information in life come from? More than sixty years later, scientists are still asking the question, even as they seek to better understand molecular life.

Organic life, it is now clear, is all about nano-technology, molecular machines, information-processing systems and, of course, DNA. As we peer into ever more sophisticated microscopes, it becomes increasingly clear that we are dealing with a carefully orchestrated process complete with a 4-bit digital code, storage, retrieval and translation mechanisms, computation protocols, and other hallmarks of a highly functional, information-rich system.

How did such a system first arise? As we noted at the beginning of this chapter, we were not around to see the first living organism appear on the early Earth and we don't have the luxury of *Star Trek's* Q to transport us back in time to witness it. But are there clues that can help us determine the origin of these living systems?

There are at least two things we know about functionally integrated, information-rich systems like those we find throughout biology—two things that can help us draw a reasonable conclusion about the origin of such systems.

First, there is no known naturalistic cause that has been shown to produce large amounts of novel information. Such a thing has never been observed. Not even once. And there is no theory successfully detailing how it might happen. Moreover, it is not as though scientists have proposed several great possibilities that just haven't quite panned out, or that several good naturalistic explanations are on the table and just need a little more tweaking or a little more research or a little more funding. Although natural processes can be called upon to explain many observations, when we are dealing with functionally integrated information-rich systems, the situation is completely different. It is not as though the search has only recently begun, we are very close, and we just need to try a little harder or look a little longer. The search has been carried out extensively over multiple generations by thousands of researchers through hundreds of thousands of hours of effort and at a cost of billions of dollars, without success. No credible naturalistic process has ever been identified that can produce information-rich systems.

Renowned synthetic organic chemist James Tour has analyzed what he sees as the most promising recent origin-of-life (OOL) research efforts. An experienced researcher with over 700 research publications and more than 130 patents to his name, he has a knack for seeing through the optimistic hype and focusing on the real-world difficulties of assembling functional molecular systems. In a 2019 critical essay, Tour expressed frustration over the lack of candor in many origin-of-life papers about the state of the field, and he asked, "Why not admit what we cannot yet explain: the mass transfer of starting materials to the molecules needed for life; the origin of life's code; the combinatorial complexities present in any living system; and the precise nonregular assembly of cellular components?" Wishful thinking, or perhaps naivete, may also play a role. "I have discussed these issues with OOL researchers," he writes, "and I am amazed that they fail to appreciate the magnitude of the problem in building molecules."[25]

Actually, the situation is even more desperate than that.

It is increasingly apparent that chance and law-like processes not only cannot *build* information-rich systems, but actually *destroy* information. On a net basis, these natural processes invariably result in a *loss* of information over time. This is a well-understood principle, observed over and over in the field. It is clear from mathematical analyses and principles of information theory. It is confirmed from lab research.

The conclusion to draw from these various observations is straightforward: processes that are either driven by a law-like cause or that come about haphazardly by chance events simply do not have the capacity to generate new information-rich systems such as those we see in biology. Based on our current understanding, we have good reasons for concluding that a purely natural explanation for these kinds of systems will *never* be found.

Indeed, in an ironic twist, it turns out that organisms have systems in place, including proofreading and error-correction mechanisms, geared specifically to combat the information-destroying tendencies of law and chance. The origin of these sophisticated proofreading and error-corrections systems also requires explanation. For someone to then turn around and suggest that law and chance produced these information-rich systems in the first place is completely upside down and backwards.

This brings us to the second thing we know. We know of only one type of cause with the demonstrated power to produce functionally integrated, information-rich systems of this sort. That cause is intelligence.

Examples abound. All around us we have desktop computers, smartphones, cloud servers, smart TVs, web-based applications, connected devices, and on and on. All of these functionally integrated systems—billions and billions of them around the world—and the information contained within them came about through a process of goal-oriented activity, preparation, planning, gathering requirements, choosing materials, creating prototypes, identifying interconnectivity protocols, and so forth. In other words, they came about through a purposeful design process, through the activity of mind. Not a single one of them came about by purely natural causes.

Even simpler information-rich artifacts, such as a book or an Instagram post—all of these trace back to a mind, an intelligence.

As Meyer has noted, "Our uniform experience affirms that specified information—whether inscribed in hieroglyphics, written in a book, encoded in a radio signal, or produced in a simulation experiment—*always* arises from an intelligent source, from a mind and not a strictly material process.... Indeed, whenever we find specified information and we know the causal story of how that information arose, we always find that it arose from an intelligent source."[26]

And note that this is a conclusion based not on ignorance or idle speculation or lack of knowledge, but on the many things we have learned and observed in molecular biology and elsewhere—on what we *know*. It is a conclusion based on our regular, repeated, and uniform experience and observations.

Whodunit?

No SCIENTIST was around at the time life was first formed on the Earth. There were no bloggers or reporters or cameras or video blogs to record the event or give us a "breaking news" report on how life started. Q from *Star Trek* can't take us back for a front-row seat of the main event. The origin of life was a historical event, one that took place long ago, far in the past and beyond our ability to witness. As a result, and as with all of the historical sciences, the way forward is to assemble clues, consider competing explanations, and carefully determine which proposed cause is the most likely, the one that most adequately explains the clues on the table.

Consider an illustration. Suppose you've recently moved to Eastern Washington from out of state, and while putting in a garden in your backyard you come across a layer of white powdery material a little way below the surface. You later find out that the same layer can be found throughout the region. You quickly run through some possible causes. A flood? A disastrous outpouring of pollutants from an old factory in town, one long ago closed down? A volcano? Each of these causes can impact a large geographic area and will affect the geology of a region. However, you quickly recognize that only one of the proposed causes has the demonstrated capacity to actually produce the effect in question. A big flood might lay down a layer of silt over a wide area, but not ash. An industrial disaster could not lay down the sheer volume of material you've encountered. Plus, industrial disasters don't produce volcanic ash, and after getting a chemist friend to run some tests, you confirm that it indeed is volcanic ash. So you draw a reasonable inference from the evidence: the white powdery ash was produced by a volcanic explosion.[27]

Notice how with careful reasoning and analysis, you can draw a reasonable inference from the physical evidence and come to the right conclusion, even if you had never heard about or witnessed that fateful Sunday morning in the spring of 1980 when Mount St. Helens erupted, sending a massive plume of ash heavenward that eventually spread as far as Canada.

As we consider the origin of life, we are like a scientist examining a deposit of ash without having been there to actually see the volcanic eruption. Because we weren't there to observe the origin of life, we can't replay a video of the event and say, "There it is. That's how it happened." But that doesn't mean we are reduced to unsupported speculations, or to throwing up our hands and giving up on the question. Instead, we can look at the clues and the evidence and draw upon our own experience to come to a reasonable conclusion—what philosophers of science call an inference to the best explanation.

In the case of the origin of life, what needs explaining isn't a layer of volcanic ash, but instead the presence of information in the first living cell. And the cause is clear, if we are but willing to entertain it. All of the many naturalistic explanations that have been proposed over the years fail to explain the information-rich systems we see in even the simplest single-celled organism. Indeed, naturalistic processes tend to degrade information over time, not create novel information. As a result, we can reasonably conclude that none of these explanations can be what philosophers of science call the "true cause," because none of them has the capacity to produce what we observe in molecular biology. However, we do know of one cause that regularly produces large amounts of information and repeatedly produces complex, functionally integrated, information-rich systems, such as we find in living cells. That cause is intelligence. Unlike the naturalistic explanations, creative intelligence can be the true, the adequate cause, because it is capable of producing these kinds of effects.

So the clear and reasonable conclusion we can draw for the origin of life and the information-rich systems we find in even the simplest organism—the inference to the best explanation—is that they were caused by the activity of an intelligent agent.

A Vanishing Act

Some proponents of the naturalistic abiogenesis story counter this information argument to design by attempting to explain away the information in DNA. In essence they try to make the information vanish. They employ either of two strategies to this end.

First, some have tried to explain away the information-rich content of DNA by arguing that there actually is no information in DNA. We might think there is information in DNA, but it isn't really there, they argue. We, as humans, are simply imposing our own biases and expectations on DNA, and really it is just a molecule like any other. What we call "information" is simply our way of understanding the molecular makeup and behavior of DNA.

If this seems to you like a strange argument, you are not alone. When Watson and Crick discovered the structure of DNA and recognized the complementary base pairing and copying mechanism, they were not just imposing their own expectations and biases on the molecules. They were discovering something that actually existed in the real world, something that was already there long before they were born and before they turned their attention to the cellular world. They certainly had no religious bias prodding them to see information in the cell. Neither man was particularly religious, both held out hope that a purely materialistic explanation for the origin of life might one day be found, and Crick even went so far as to suggest that the first life on Earth was seeded from outer space, having originated on some faraway planet. This idea only backs up the problem to another planet, and it adds the additional difficulty of safely transporting microscopic life across untold millions of miles of cold space while it's being bombarded by harmful cosmic rays. But the fact that he was willing to reach for such an explanation clearly shows that this was not a man eager to acknowledge purposeful design as an explanation for the origin of life on Earth. And yet he and Watson readily acknowledged that the cell is rich with information and information-processing systems.

Subsequent discoveries have only confirmed and deepened that understanding. Thus, it has been known for decades that there is information in DNA—real, observable, encoded, functional information. Numerous successful companies have been founded to retrieve, study, and analyze the information in DNA. University biology departments and even some computer departments have created courses to teach the next generation of scientists about the information in DNA. An entire field of research called "bioinformatics" has arisen in recent years, dedicated to the study of information in biological systems, in particular the information in DNA.

Other opponents of design in biology have taken just the opposite tack, arguing that there is information in everything. The assumption behind this argument is that all matter in the universe contains information—the rocks, the particles, the stars, and the galaxies. Sure, DNA contains information, they argue, but so does everything else. So there is nothing unique about DNA. Nothing to see here, folks. Move along.

One person I've debated argued, for example, that DNA is just a molecule like any other molecule and that there is nothing more interesting in DNA than in a glass of salt water, because, as he claimed, there is information in both DNA and salt water.

This, too, is nonsense. Even a child can readily understand that there is a world of difference between what we find in DNA and what we see in something like a glass of salt water or the particles of lifeless matter floating about the universe.[28] It's the same difference as between the letters in a meaningful book and page after page of random characters (in the case of particles floating haphazardly about the universe), or (in the case of salt water) page after page of a relatively simple pattern of repeating letters—for example, aabbccdd, aabbccdd, aabbccdd repeating over and over.

In contrast to these non-living examples, what we find in DNA is neither a simple repeating pattern nor a random collection of nucleotides. Instead, DNA contains highly specified, functional information stored directly in digital form and expressed through the genetic code.

How did the information we find in cells arise in the first place? The question persists. Any attempt to ignore it or to sweep it under the rug by denying or trivializing the existence of biological information is intellectually empty and gives us a hint that perhaps there is some other agenda than open-minded scientific inquiry at play.

Coming Full Circle

Today, with the tremendous developments over the last few decades in our understanding of DNA and the genetic code, along with the discovery of ingenious molecular machines at the cellular level, we are better positioned than ever before to answer the question at the beginning of this chapter: How did life begin? The accumulated evidence we have today points toward a planned, purposeful, carefully designed origin of life as the best explanation.

There are many origin-of-life researchers who reject this conclusion, but they do so primarily by insisting dogmatically that scientists must only entertain purely naturalistic, mindless processes to explain the origin of life. Their claim that life arose on the early Earth through a long series of unguided chemical interactions is hardly more valid than the distant speculations of our ancient forebears about spontaneous generation. Actually, it's arguably less valid because modern materialists no longer have the excuse of ignorance. People once thought that life routinely emerged from non-life. We now know better. And no further back than Darwin's time many scientists assumed that microscopic life was fairly simple. Now we know that even the simplest cell is a marvel of information processing and engineering sophistication.

Despite Darwin's creative conjectures about the first cell, despite the theories of Oparin and Haldane, and the careful experiments of Miller and Urey, despite the subsequent decades of discovery—and indeed, in large part because of those discoveries—it's clearer than ever that something more than time and blind material processes are required to conjure up the first living cell.

When we step away from the vague proposals and speculations from the past and examine what is actually required for a living organism—what is actually required to assemble a complex, functional, information-rich organism—the answer is clear. The first life was not an accident of chemistry or a lucky draw of the cosmic lottery. Rather, life was intended. It was planned. It was orchestrated.

It was designed.

Review: Your Turn

1. How do scientists investigate and reason about past events that they can never directly observe, such as the origin of the first life on Earth?

2. Why is the assumption that life must have started by purely natural processes, without any intelligent guidance or intervention, a philosophical assumption rather than a scientific one?

3. Instead of assuming that life must have originated by purely natural processes, what evidence can we consider to determine whether this is true or whether life required a creative intelligence?

4. Did the Miller-Urey experiment show that life could arise on the early Earth by natural causes? What did it show?

5. What does DNA contain that makes it so different from non-living matter?

6. Even the simplest cells are brimming with information. What type of cause has the demonstrated ability to generate new information?

3. A Factory That Builds Factories That Build Factories That...

Eric H. Anderson

Nobel Prize recipient and Harvard origin-of-life researcher Jack Szostak once remarked, "In my lab, we're interested in the transition from chemistry to early biology on the early earth.... You want something that can grow and divide and, most importantly, exhibit Darwinian evolution."[1]

Another noted origin-of-life researcher, Gerald F. Joyce, says much the same thing. When asked about the idea that chemicals might have come together on the early Earth to form something that could copy itself, Joyce responded, "That's what we and others are interested in because that's sort of, you know, the tipping point between chemistry before and biology after."[2]

Self-replication, then, is not just one more in a long list of problems to be solved for the origin of life. As far as many of the leading origin-of-life researchers are concerned, discovering the pathway to a self-replicating entity is the central challenge, the Holy Grail. Figure out how to get that from purely natural processes, and the hope is that everything else will take care of itself.

But it's a Grail that continues to elude the research community, despite the brash claims occasionally made to the contrary.

Dawkins's Miracle Molecule

A few years ago I happened to turn on my car radio and caught the end of a lecture segment on public radio. Evolutionary biologist and prominent atheist Richard Dawkins was the guest. Dawkins held the position of Professor for the Public Understanding of Science at Oxford University for more than a decade, and one of the questions posed to him made me quickly reach over and turn up the volume.

"How close are we to understanding the origin of life?" the moderator asked.

I half-expected Dawkins to acknowledge the many difficulties with abiogenesis, to admit that this was a huge open question, and to confess that we don't yet have any good abiogenesis scenarios, while claiming, as so many proponents of evolution do, that the origin of life is a separate question from biological evolution. That is, I thought he might concede the many widely acknowledged difficulties still facing the origin of life but try to contain the damage for the materialistic outlook by emphasizing that at least things were well in hand for evolutionary theory after the origin of the first life.

To my surprise, Dawkins responded rather glibly that we have a pretty good idea how life started. Yes, there are some challenges, he acknowledged, but we know what happened in broad strokes and at this point, he implied, we are basically filling in the details.

Having studied the origin of life at length and being aware of the many and acute problems with abiogenesis theories, it struck me as more than a little irresponsible for someone wearing the title of "Professor for the Public Understanding of Science" to claim in a public venue to thousands of listeners that we have a pretty good idea how life started.

Why would Dawkins make a statement like that? Was he purposely misinforming listeners about the current state of the science, or was he unaware of the many problems with abiogenesis? Did he really believe what he was saying?

As I analyzed the question further in the coming days, I realized that Dawkins's thinking likely stems from the notion that the origin of life—at least the initial starting event—was a relatively simple event. Not necessarily a common event or an easily repeatable event, mind you, but a relatively simple one.

In his book *The Selfish Gene*, Dawkins paints a picture remarkably similar to Darwin's statement in his 1871 letter to Joseph Hooker (quoted in the previous chapter). "Nowadays large organic molecules would not last long enough to be noticed: they would be quickly absorbed and broken down by bacteria or other living creatures," Dawkins writes. "But bacteria and the rest of us are late-comers, and in those days [on the early Earth] large organic molecules could drift unmolested[3] through the thickening broth."[4]

With this assumed backdrop of early Earth conditions, Dawkins goes on to suggest the first key step in the origin of life: "At some point a particularly remarkable molecule was formed by accident. We will call it the *Replicator*. It may not necessarily have been the biggest or the most complex molecule around, but it had the extraordinary property of being able to create copies of itself."[5]

This hypothetical self-replicating molecule is crucial to the materialist creation story, and on two counts. First, getting a complete organism to arise by chance is, as is widely acknowledged, too unlikely and never could have occurred. So something simpler, something that had a much greater likelihood of arising by pure chance, something like a simple self-replicating molecule, had to kick-start the process. Second, once this self-replicating molecule came on the scene, then Darwinian evolution could kick in, bringing the impressive power of random mutations and natural selection to eventually transform our simple self-replicating molecule into an actual organism.

At least that is how the story goes.

This "particularly remarkable molecule," Dawkins suggests, is easy to imagine, and the remainder of his description of this extraordinary entity consists of a simple, though chemically unrealistic, thought experiment about how such a fascinating molecule might work, making copies of itself, "competing" with other molecules in the watery environment, and so on.

Origin-of-life researchers, to their credit, haven't been satisfied with thought experiments alone. There has been a great deal of effort expended over the past couple of decades trying to create a self-replicating molecule in the lab, and then to apply the lessons learned to the question of the origin of life. Some good work has been done and some interesting results occasionally published, but nobody has been able to create such a molecule.

To be sure, there have been several papers published and news stories released proclaiming that researchers have created this or that self-replicating molecule, but these claims invariably turn out to be misleading. If anyone has actually discovered or created a self-replicating molecule, they are keeping it a very good secret.

This failure to produce such a molecule, keep in mind, is despite decades of research and lavish financial expenditure. The reason for the failure is not for lack of time, effort, and funding. No, the reason is much more fundamental.

The Blob Has a Secret

As we saw in the previous chapter, there was a sense in Darwin's day that microorganisms were rather simple, each one little more than a tiny "blob of protoplasm."[6] Darwin viewed the organism as a flexible conglomeration of these simple cells. Through no fault of their own, he and his contemporaries of the time knew nothing of genetic information processing, signaling, and feedbacks, nothing of cellular machinery, integrated systems, complex coordination of molecular parts, or the many other requirements for even the simplest working cell.

In *The Origin of Species* Darwin described organisms as "plastic."[7] He wasn't referring to the material used to make children's toys today, but rather to the idea that organisms were flexible and could, he was convinced, be readily shaped and molded by natural selection to essentially any form. From this viewpoint it followed that adding more cells or making changes to the organism should also be a relatively simple process.

However, with the accumulating knowledge of cellular structures in the late 1800s, the discoveries of cellular systems and proteins and metabolic pathways, the unraveling of DNA's structure in the 1950s, and the subsequent discoveries up to the present that continue to uncover new depths of biological complexity, it became ever clearer that cells are anything but simple, and that even the humblest organism is complex beyond anything previously imagined. Not just complex. Complex and coordinated, with a 4-bit digital code, information storage, retrieval and translation mechanisms, error-correction algorithms, functionally integrated systems, and molecular machines—marvels of nanotechnology that put to shame anything humans have yet created.

As a result of these discoveries it became increasingly clear that no organism, even a relatively simple single-celled organism, could arise all at once on the early Earth by chance.

But if life couldn't arise by chance as a single event, perhaps a series of events could do the trick. Perhaps if the problem were broken down into simpler steps then it might be possible?

With that thought firmly in mind, abiogenesis proponents busily churned out hypothesis after hypothesis that might help the process along, simpler steps that could perhaps lead to something more. In other words, rather than attempting to explain how a simple single-celled organism could arise by chance, many origin-of-life researchers focused on identifying what the initial capacity or characteristic of the earliest stage of life likely was. As we saw in the previous chapter, information storage and processing seem to be central to all life forms. So perhaps life started with DNA. Other researchers noted that life needed a way to obtain and use energy to run cellular processes. So perhaps the key to the origin of life was a primitive form of metabolism. Still other researchers focused on the fact that organisms needed a way to protect themselves from the surrounding environment and protect the tender early chemical reactions from interference. So perhaps life had to start with a protective shell or bubble, some kind of early cell membrane.

One of the more promising ideas emerged from the discovery that some RNA molecules could act as enzymes, helping catalyze chemical reactions in the cell. Since RNA could also store information, similar to DNA, it seemed ideally suited to perform not just one, but two roles in the abiogenesis story. So perhaps, it was suggested, life started as an RNA molecule.

These and other ideas continue to be developed today, with regular press releases and articles gracing the pages of popular news sites and prominent scientific journals. Without minimizing the importance of any particular avenue of research, it is nevertheless safe to say that the most prominent view today among origin-of-life researchers is essentially the same that Dawkins outlined in *The Selfish Gene*—namely, life started with a molecule, some kind of self-replicating molecule.

Darwinian Evolution All the Way Down

THE CURRENT evolutionary view of life, although much more attuned to the complexity and information-rich properties of organisms than was the science of Darwin's time, is still very much dependent on the same two assumptions Darwin made so long ago: *First, if we start with a simple entity it will eventually undergo variations sufficient in both kind and quantity to turn it into another organism; indeed, to eventually turn it into everything we see in biology today. Second, organisms are very flexible in their makeup, able to undergo innumerable changes over time and incorporate those changes into their makeup without breaking down or missing any steps in the long chain of required changes.*

Based on these two fundamental assumptions, the thinking among current origin-of-life researchers is that if we can just get a self-replicating molecule on the early Earth, then the Darwinian process of mutations and natural selection can take over and, eventually, produce the first living organism. Then that first living organism will of course go on to produce everything we see around us in nature...

Don't misunderstand. There is serious doubt (as we will explore later in this chapter and the subsequent chapters of this book) whether the evolutionary mechanism can actually transform a self-replicating molecule into a living organism and produce the kinds of systems we see in living beings. But the vision of natural selection having near-mystical powers of creation has taken such hold on the evolutionary imagination that many researchers seem to believe that with the magic wand of natural selection, "all things are possible." Stated another way, it is not that there is actually any good evidence that a self-replicating molecule can give rise to complex life; it is just that once natural selection kicks in, the idea becomes more believable to many people.

As a result, many prominent origin-of-life researchers today view the origin of life as essentially a problem of getting a single self-replicating molecule. Once a self-replicating molecule appears on the hazy scene of the early Earth, the power of Darwinian evolution is thought to take over and then... anything goes.

Thus does an article discussing origin-of-life research by David Horning and Gerald Joyce observe, "Research into the origin of life takes for granted that the first living thing was much simpler than any existing life... At some point, one molecule acquired the ability to replicate itself from chemicals found on the primordial Earth. Once that took place, Darwinian evolution could take over."[8]

With that assumption firmly in place, the self-replicating molecule takes on the central role in the dramatic history of life on Earth, and self-replication becomes the key to the entire abiogenesis story.

Most criticisms of abiogenesis over the years have focused on the reducing atmosphere, energy sources, the difficulty of forming life-essential polymers in the primordial soup, the existence of the necessary nucleotides or amino acids at the right place and time, the rise of coding and information-rich molecules, the astronomical odds against getting molecules joined up in the right order, and so on.

However, much less time has been spent on the issue of self-replication. Indeed, even most critics of abiogenesis largely ignore the issue or appear to accept unreflectively the idea that self-replication may indeed be an early step on the path to the first life.

Evolutionary proponents, for their part, hesitated to take on the challenge of abiogenesis for many decades. Indeed, for debating purposes many refused to grapple with it, arguing that the origin of life is a problem that stands completely apart from evolution and need not be addressed by evolutionary proponents because evolution only starts once there is a living organism. But the formidable challenges with abiogenesis have forced its proponents to fall back on what they view as the most powerful force of creativity: Darwinian evolution in the form of natural selection acting on variations arising within self-reproducing entities thought to exist before the first living cell. The hope is that in this way Darwinian evolution can solve the difficult challenge of getting that initial living organism in the first place, a challenge that includes creating metabolism, cellular systems, and pages and pages of precisely coded, high-functioning digital information.

So, rather than being irrelevant to the origin-of-life story, Darwinian evolution is now viewed as central to it—a last-ditch effort to hold together the many rapidly unraveling threads of the abiogenesis tapestry. This marks a significant shift in the rhetorical underpinnings of the materialist creation story.

It is true that earlier researchers such as Oparin, Haldane, and other abiogenesis proponents had at times described the origin-of-life process as some kind of chemical "evolution." Yet any connection between such a chemical evolutionary process and Darwinian evolution long remained tenuous at best. Indeed, many scientists and theorists over the years explicitly rejected the application of Darwinian evolution to the time period before the existence of the first living organism, drawing a bright line between the problem of the origin of life and the evolution of life following its origin.[9]

This is no longer the case. Under the current paradigm, abiogenesis begins with undirected chemical reactions, leading by chance to a simple self-replicator, such as a self-replicating molecule of some kind. Abiogenesis proponents imagine natural selection stepping in at that point to help the tender molecule acquire additional traits, eventually leading to the first living organism and then from there to the full complexity and diversity of life we see today.

So, rather than having a living organism and then endowing that organism with an *additional* ability of self-replication, the materialistic abiogenesis story makes self-replication the first ability. Self-replication thus becomes the initial formative characteristic of the ancestral entity of all life, the characteristic from which all other subsequent features and powers arise.

Three Indispensables... Actually, Four

WHAT WOULD it take for a chemical unit on the early Earth to achieve the ability to self-replicate? That's no small challenge. Some have pointed to crystals, autocatalytic reactions, and even RNA ligase molecules.[10] But despite interesting chemical and structural properties, none of these actually self-replicates.

A number of researchers have considered what might be required of even the simplest truly self-replicating chemical entity. Here are three core requirements: (1) It has to be able to form under natural conditions, without help from a lab technician. (2) It has to be able to make copies of itself by locating and ordering specific atoms or small molecules that would be available in the environment, not by simply catalyzing a reaction between carefully designed and previously prepared sections of itself, as in so many of the lab experiments carried out in recent years. (3) It has to be stable enough to exist in real-world conditions on the early Earth—the "primordial soup"—without breaking down too quickly and without getting bogged down by interfering cross-reactions.

Additionally, if the molecule is to jump-start a Darwinian process of mutation and natural selection, it must have the capacity to mutate while somehow retaining the ability to faithfully replicate its now-mutated self.

Based on extensive research performed by many origin-of-life researchers over the past couple of decades, there are good reasons to conclude that a single molecule alone could not manage all this.[11] Note, too, that the above is only a summary list of requirements. A comprehensive list would fill many pages.[12]

The challenge in origin-of-life studies is to self-replicate a self-replicator, which can in turn self-replicate a self-replicator, *ad infinitum*. The equivalent would be a computer that can self-replicate itself, the copies of which could self-replicate themselves, on and on. And indeed, not just computers but fully functional robots.

Some might be tempted to point to a computer virus or other computer program that can copy itself, but such programs are not self-replicating in any substantive sense. The software program only exists and runs on a carefully designed and functional piece of hardware that is certainly not replicated in the process. Further, there is generally an operating system, as well as several additional layers of software in the form of drivers, compilers, interfaces, middleware, and so on. The most that can be said for so-called "self-replicating" computer programs is this: a carefully designed and functionally integrated system of hardware and software can reproduce a copy of *a portion* of the software on the machine. Interesting, yes, but essentially irrelevant to the problem at hand.

True self-replication is a more onerous task. Once we consider the task of actually building a self-replicating machine that can exist in the real world in physical, three-dimensional space, the challenges become a bit more evident.

A 3D Printer That Prints... 3D Printers?

To HELP us understand what is involved in self-replication, let's set aside for a moment the dizzying complexity of the living cell and consider what would be involved in building the simplest possible self-replicating machine with our existing technology.

The ability to engineer a self-replicating machine has been the topic of much discussion in science fiction stories and movies, ranging from the large and powerful Terminator-style robots to small but deadly nanites. It remains that—science fiction. But will it always be so?

There are now 3D printers with the ability to create some of their own parts in three-dimensional space. This has, for the first time in human history, allowed us to begin dreaming in concrete terms of taking the first steps on the long and still baffling road to creating a self-replicating machine. Is such a feat even possible? It sounds fantastic, even crazy, but the fantastical idea is driving some fascinating research. And what we are learning has direct implications for research on what would be minimally required for the first self-reproducing entity in the history of life.

First, a bit of background on 3D printing for those new to the field.

I became interested in 3D printing years ago and have followed the development of the industry off and on ever since. Recently the technology has become cheap enough that 3D printers have moved into the world of the hobbyist and the technology enthusiast. Popular consumer-level printers include MakerBot, FlashForge, Creality3D, and many others.

At the time I am writing this, 3D printers range from personal machines costing a few hundred dollars that produce rough prints in a single material to high-end professional printers costing many thousands of dollars boasting sub-50-micron resolution and printing in multiple materials. Several different kinds of 3D printing technologies also ex-

Figure 3.1. 3D printed stand designed by the author on an early extrusion printer.

ist, from material extrusion (the most common technology for consumer and prosumer printers, and the one that you have probably seen many times), to powder bed fusion, photo-polymerization, ultrasonic additive, material jetting, electron beam melting, and more.

Several years ago our local library received a grant to educate library patrons on the technology of 3D printers by allowing patrons to reserve print time, so I took advantage of the opportunity to design and print a simple stand for one of my 5x5x5 cubes (basically a Rubik's cube on steroids).

This is an exciting and explosive technology that promises to transform the landscape of design and prototyping activities, and even some manufacturing processes. There are a lot of daring engineers and visionaries in the field, but perhaps among the most daring are those involved in the RepRap Project, an open-source venture that seeks to create a self-replicating 3D printer.[13] Many people have been involved in this project and have done tremendous work in moving it forward, with significant strides made. Many of the parts for a RepRap printer can be printed on the printer itself to reasonable tolerances, enabling a hobbyist to use those parts in the construction of a new printer.

However, as is often the case with groundbreaking new technologies, the excitement around potential future breakthroughs tends to intrude into assessments of on-the-ground realities. For example, the RepRap website touts the machine as "humanity's first general-purpose self-replicating manufacturing machine." In an allusion to evolutionary thinking, and ignoring the tremendous amount of design and engineering involved in producing RepRap, one of the early RepRap printers was even named "Darwin."

Another interesting printer, the Kickstarter-backed BI V2.0,[14] received breathless attention in late 2013, with a myriad of headlines touting "The World's First Self-Replicating 3D Printer!" This isn't just sloppy newswire enthusiasm; even the official project website touted BI V2.0 as "a self-replicating, high precision 3D Printer."[15]

If one is the trusting sort, it's tempting to look at projects like RepRap or BI V2.0 and think, "Wow! We are almost there. We've nearly created a self-replicating machine!" But a closer look is warranted. Neither RepRap nor BI V2.0 are self-replicating.

Not in theory or in practice.

Not even close.

Not even in the ballpark.

Don't get me wrong. I love this technology. I've followed RepRap closely and consider it a fantastic idea and an excellent open-source project. I even considered contributing funds to the BI V2.0 Kickstarter project when it first came out. But despite impressive efforts, a human-designed self-replicating machine remains a long way off.

Finding the Ballpark

MANY REPRAP users have shared online photographs of the many parts of the RepRap printer that can be printed on the printer itself in a hard plastic material, like ABS plastic.[16] An impressive number of parts can be printed, to be sure. Yet even a cursory analysis of the printing process reveals that the printer is not actually able to print any of those parts by itself.

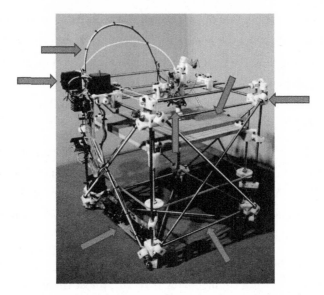

Figure 3.2. RepRap printer with arrows pointing to just a few of the many parts that cannot be printed on the printer.

The printer must first be set up and programmed with the right parameters, and it must be fed the material for extrusion. Even after parts are printed, they must be carefully removed from the print bed by the user, inspected for quality and, in many cases, cleaned up or sanded before they are ready as usable parts. So the impressive number of parts that can be printed doesn't tell the whole story.

What's more, many of the printer's other parts cannot be printed by the printer, with or without help. These include structural support rods, screws, copper wire, rubber drive belts, a precision stainless steel extrusion nozzle, a print bed, a heating element, clamps and ties, and a filament feeder.

More daunting still, the printer requires a circuit board, an SD card reader, cabling, control switches, electric motors, and more in order to function.

The printer is not even close to being able to produce all those parts.

And the situation is even worse than all those problems would suggest.

An electric motor by itself is a precision machine that requires multiple parts, manufactured to tight tolerances and assembled in just the right way in order to function. Even a simple electric motor includes a housing, shaft, rotor, stator, terminals, magnets, copper windings, some kind of lubricant and/or bearings, and wiring connections.

More daunting still, a printed circuit board is a marvel of modern engineering and includes thermoset resin laminate materials, a battery, resistors, transistors, capacitors, inductors, diodes, switches, and more—all manufactured to precise tolerances.

Finally, for our printer to be truly self-replicating, it must be able to work in multiple materials. It is one thing to print parts in plastic and to have the right nozzle and heating element to do that. It is quite another to print parts in multiple materials. If our printer were truly self-replicating, it would be able to work not only in plastic, but also in aluminum, stainless steel, copper, rubber, silver, gold, tin, and fiberglass. It also would need the ability to safely handle zinc chloride, hydrochloric acid, resin laminates, and etching chemicals.

This is only a partial list of missing requirements.

Now, it's true that savvy engineers and designers often can find ways to substitute different materials and in different ways, so it's possible to find a few workarounds that would trim down the total number of different parts and materials. To that end, some enterprising individuals have created offshoots of RepRap that use plastic in place of the steel support rods and the rubber belts. This is clever design work. But remember, these workarounds are limited in their application, the description above is just a very partial sketch, and a detailed analysis would reveal many more parts and materials required for a truly self-replicating printer.

The point here is not to dog on RepRap. As I said, I'm a fan. The point is to provide the reader with a sense of the challenge involved and the scale of the problem. Whichever printer we are analyzing and which-ever parts list we want to focus on, we find that creating even a relatively modest machine that can produce all of its own parts is an astounding engineering challenge—a challenge far beyond anything our best engineers and brightest minds can presently accomplish.

Putting It All Together

If we are hoping to ever build a self-replicating machine, there is another aspect of the process we will have to master that goes beyond replicating the parts. Even if our printer had the remarkable ability to print multiple materials at the sub-micron level, and print every single part used in the construction of the printer—something which at this stage is but a distant dream—it would still not be able to assemble itself. To be truly self-replicating, it would also need to be able to assemble those parts in actual, physical, three-dimensional space.

To do that, the printer would need to have carefully controlled and sophisticated robotic assembly systems. For example, it would need an assembly arm to pick up the printed pieces, analyze them for complete-ness and quality, rotate them into the right position, and place them in the correct location. In reality, this would require multiple assembly arms and mechanisms.

Also, as soon as we introduce a new assembly arm and its many attendant parts into the mix, we then have an entire additional set of machine parts that in turn have to be incorporated into our printer de-sign, printed, and assembled. It also would require additional computer software. And that software, that digital information, would be far from simple. Indeed, the entire printer would need to be radically re-engi-neered to account for these additional parts and mechanisms.

Worse, every time we include a new part or an additional mecha-nism to assist with this challenging self-replication process, that new part or mechanism also must be replicated, requiring additional instruc-tion sets, perhaps a reworking of the machine's physical layout, and additional information related to this new part or mechanism: how it is to be constructed, how it is to be assembled, how it is to function.

Indeed, every single time we add a significant new part, or in the vernacular of the materialistic evolution story, every time the nascent organism evolves a new meaningful function, that new function requires not only a careful integration into the whole, but the instruction set to implement and reproduce the parts necessary for that new function.

Further, it is unclear how the printer could even accomplish the assembly without additional significant re-engineering. Remember, the printer occupies a physical three-dimensional space. The best it can do is assemble a copy right next to itself, with the far side of the copy some 12 to 24 inches away. Thus, any assembly mechanism would have to be able to reach outside of the box—outside of itself—in order to reproduce itself. This suggests another challenge.

In-House Engineering

A 3D printer assembling a copy outside of itself might work on a clean tabletop with no other interference, but such an approach is unfortunately completely unworkable in the fluid and watery biological environment. So the cell uses an ingenious approach. It constructs a copy of itself inside of itself, using its own cell membrane to form the protective environment for construction, and then divides by drawing the cell membrane inward between the original and the copy, eventually sealing off the gap and releasing the now completed copy into the larger environment.

This approach allows the cell to faithfully self-replicate while avoiding disastrous interfering cross-reactions with other chemicals and molecules in the environment. It also keeps the cellular components from drifting apart and being lost in the watery environment.

In a living bacterial cell, for example, the cell expands and the necessary inner components of the cell are faithfully replicated (including DNA). After the cellular components separate into separate ends of the cell, the center of the cell is divided and sealed off by a septum—a new cell wall and new membrane material separating the two halves—until it is completely sealed and the two cells are separated.

Compare this replication process to our hypothetical self-replicating 3D printer. It would be as though our printer, basically a cube-like structure, were to expand its own frame to encompass a space the size of two printers, construct and assemble the new internal components in that protected space, and then rebuild two walls between the identical sections in order to release the completed copy into the environment. This would be a remarkable engineering feat indeed!

Finally, a truly autonomous self-replicating entity must also be able to locate, acquire, and make use of raw materials for construction of new parts, and generate its own power from materials available in the environment. No convenient electrical cord plugged into the wall, please. Nor any careful feeding of the printer filament by a user. And for long-term successful replication over more than just a few generations, it would be critical to have numerous feedback and quality control mechanisms, error correction capabilities, and the like.

The above is only a very partial outline of what would be involved in building a truly self-replicating machine. But as we think through some of these details—an exercise that is, unfortunately, too often skipped by abiogenesis enthusiasts—we begin to grasp the scale of the problem. As we do so, and wonder if such an engineering feat is even possible, we should not overlook the elephant in the room: the creation of a 3D printer that could print all of its parts and also assemble all of those parts into another self-replicating 3D printer, and successfully do this generation after generation—as even the simplest self-replicating cell can do—would be a most impressive work of ingenious design.

Wanted: Molecular Unicorn, Purple

WHILE THERE are important differences between the macro world of 3D printing and the micro world of the cell, our brief review of what would be involved in creating a truly self-replicating machine in the macro world gives us a sense of the many abilities a self-replicating molecule would need to possess to be truly viable. For instance, the molecule would need to identify, position, and orient the correct individual building blocks. It would then need to link them together. In a liquid environment, the linking could not occur without accessing some energy source for assembling the blocks together. And among the many other capacities it would need to possess, the molecule would need the ability to error-check the developing duplicate molecule to prevent the essential information from degrading each time it was copied.[17]

The exercise casts into doubt the notion that a solitary molecule, however large and sophisticated, could pull off the task. For starters, it would lack a cell wall to protect itself from the violent buffeting of the surrounding chemical soup and the unavoidable interfering cross-reactions. If it somehow possessed every other needed feature of a viable self-replicating machine, it would have to be orders of magnitude more complex—more sophisticated—than any existing organic molecule. And since the whole point of proposing this purple unicorn of a molecule is to suggest a potentially plausible pathway for blind natural forces to kick-start life, then the question before us isn't whether an intelligent agent could ever assemble such a remarkably capable hypothetical molecule, but whether mindless natural forces could somehow produce it, and do so before the Darwinian process of random variation and natural selection could help, since remember, that process only begins once a self-replicating entity is in place and doing its thing.

What sort of super-molecule would be required? Neither DNA nor RNA, after all, comes even close to having the full suite of capacities needed to self-replicate all by itself. Each needs the other, and each needs the cell.

What is the cell? It's a work of nanotechnology beyond anything humans have ever built. The geneticist Michael Denton described it as a "an object of unparalleled complexity and adaptive design." Denton invites us to imagine that we greatly magnify a cell so that we could see all of the cell's components working together:

> What we would be witnessing would be an object resembling an immense automated factory, a factory larger than a city and carrying out almost as many unique functions as all the manufacturing activities of man on earth. However, it would be a factory which would have one capacity not equaled in any of our own most advanced machines, for it would be capable of replicating its entire structure within a matter of a few hours. To witness such an act... would be an awe-inspiring spectacle.[18]

Having walked through just some of the technological requirements of a truly self-replicating 3D printer, this shouldn't surprise us. When we observe that a cell can self-replicate, we can begin to ask what technologies, what capacities, would be required for that to be possible. The list is long and daunting. The sophistication of the cell is wondrous.

Researchers have attempted to identify the minimal requirements for a living cell by methodically removing proteins and seeing whether the cell continues to function. For a relatively simple parasite that depends upon its host for survival, researchers identified over 300 essential proteins.[19] Another research group studied one of the smallest and simplest free-living bacteria and estimated that twice as many proteins were required.[20] Even if we take the smaller estimate, that would still mean that over 300 different kinds of molecules are required for a relatively simple self-replicating cell, not to mention the DNA molecule and the genetic instructions it contains. The idea that a single molecule could ever perform such a task stretches the imagination.[21]

Those obsessed with the possibility of a self-replicating molecule have to ignore all of the careful analysis provided above. They have to ignore the reality that self-replication, rather than being a simple kick-starting point at the beginning of the long road of evolution, lies at the end of an extremely complicated, sophisticated, and specified engineering process. And they have to ignore the fact that every time a significant new biological feature is acquired or something is added to assist in the self-replication process, the very addition requires a reworking of the self-replication process itself, along with the likely addition of new components and additional information to self-replicate the new parts.[22] This fact, rarely discussed or acknowledged in the evolutionary literature, not only casts doubt on the materialistic origin-of-life story, but also represents a fundamental conceptual problem for the evolutionary process thereafter.

The idea that self-replication is the starting point for the origin of life is not just questionable. It is not just one more in a long list of problems with the abiogenesis story. It does not just make the odds worse. It is completely upside down and backwards. It is diametrically opposed to the physical, chemical, and engineering realities.

So why do many origin-of-life researchers remain fixated on the purple unicorn of a self-replicating molecule? Regrettably, in the area of abiogenesis it is the theory instead of the evidence that drives the thinking. This is why Richard Dawkins could confidently claim in *The Selfish Gene* that "a molecule that makes copies of itself is not as difficult to imagine as it seems at first, and it only had to arise once."[23] Yes, imagine. The theory just requires some imagination and a strong dose of luck.

It's why so much energy in origin-of-life research today is focused on finding this elusive self-replicating molecule. The insistence on a materialistic origin of life, coupled with the hypnotic allure of the supposedly limitless power of natural selection, leads the materialist to draw a conclusion that is not only unsupported, but diametrically opposed to the physical, chemical, and engineering realities we see in the world around us. That is, it flies in the face of what we know both from engineering and from observing the simplest self-replicating bacteria, each a marvel of engineering sophistication.

Self-replication, contrary to the materialist abiogenesis story, is not the *beginning* feature, a rudimentary trait that a single molecule could handle. Rather it is a *culminating* trait, one of the most dazzlingly high-tech traits in the biosphere. The accumulated evidence, taken together, strongly suggests that self-replication lies at the end of a very complicated, deeply integrated, highly sophisticated, thoughtfully planned, carefully controlled engineering process.

In the end, the abiogenesis story is not just incomplete, with details remaining to be filled in. No. The abiogenesis paradigm, with its placement of self-replication as the first stage of development, is fundamentally flawed at a conceptual level. It is opposed to both the evidence and our real-world experience and needs to be discarded.

Review: Your Turn

1. What is abiogenesis?

2. What is attractive about the idea that Darwinian evolution began with a simple self-replicating molecule, rather than a living organism?

3. According to abiogenesis researchers, is Darwinian evolution relevant to the origin of life? How?

4. How close are we to being able to create a truly autonomous, self-replicating machine? What are some challenges that still remain?

5. What problems, if any, are there with the idea of nature producing a relatively simple, self-replicating molecule?

4. Irreducible Complexity and Evolution

Robert P. Waltzer

You may have heard it said that evolution is a fact. The most reasonable response to such a statement isn't yea or nay. It's, what do you mean by *evolution?* That's because the term *evolution* can mean many different things. It can refer to change over time in the plants and animals that have existed on earth. It can refer to relatively small changes within species. It can refer to the origin of fundamentally new species from earlier forms. It can refer to the common ancestry of all life on earth.

More specifically, it may refer to the theory that natural selection acting on small variations over millions of generations explains the origin and diversity of all life—a theory first propounded by Charles Darwin and Alfred Russel Wallace in the nineteenth century, and further developed and refined in the subsequent 160 years.[1] Finally, the term may refer to some extended version of this theory, one that involves the natural selection/variation mechanism but also other natural mechanisms.

So the term *evolution* can refer to many different things. Being aware of this can help us navigate discussions of evolutionary theory, clear away some of the fog that often bedevils conversations on the topic, and equip us to better assess claims for and against evolutionary theory. To that end, let's briefly unpack a few of the most common meanings of the term: change over time, common descent, natural selection, microevolution, and macroevolution.

Change Over Time

DIFFERENT PLANT and animal forms existed at different periods of geological history. Nobody seriously questions this claim. For example, if we look at the cat family (Felidae), some species became extinct, such as the Smilodon (known colloquially as the saber-toothed tiger), and others appeared more recently. So members of the cat family were not always the same throughout geological history. This sort of change over time is often described by the term *evolution*. Notice that, by itself, such changes over time say nothing about what drove the change or whether some or all of the different life forms in the history of life share a common ancestry. Change over time is a very modest claim about the history of life on earth, one that few if any question.

Common Descent

IT'S WIDELY believed that cats—from lions to panthers to domestic cats and everything in between—share a common ancestor. Going beyond the cat family and extending this kind of relatedness to all species, most of Darwin's followers argued that there was a common ancestor for all life on earth,[2] an idea known as universal common descent. This was not a new idea with Darwin, but it gained extra weight after Darwin and Wallace proposed their theory of evolution,[3] and sometimes when somebody refers to "evolution," they mean the idea that all life evolved from a common ancestor. (Note, however, that one can affirm common ancestry without endorsing any particular account of how this occurred. A person might, for instance, think the process was intelligently guided.)

Natural Selection

IN NATURE, there is often a competition for limited resources. Some members of a species possess this or that helpful variation, which makes them better at obtaining these resources. This, in turn, makes them more likely to survive and reproduce. The ones with the beneficial variations are thus more likely to pass on their beneficial variation to future generations. The beneficial variations are thus selected and the harmful ones filtered out. That's the idea of natural selection in a nutshell.

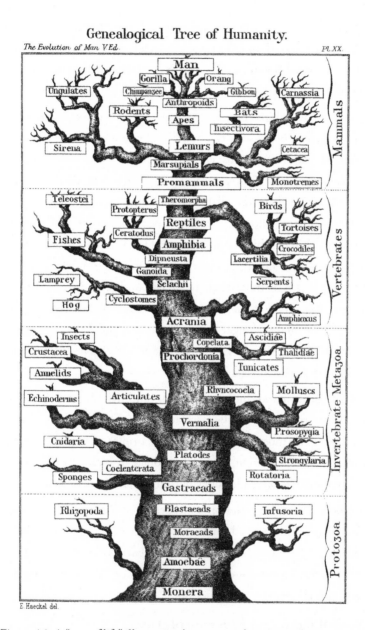

Figure 4.1. A "tree of life" illustration by nineteenth-century German naturalist
Ernst Haeckel, depicting the idea that all species and groups of species
arose from a common ancestor. Then and now, there is a certain amount of
speculation in the production of such illustrations, and much disagreement
among evolutionary theorists as to what to place where in the tree.

As Darwin noted, when a variation helps a creature survive and reproduce, that variation, called a selective advantage, is thereby more likely to get passed down to offspring and eventually become common in a population.

Let's consider a bird species in an environment where a shift in climate has led to an increase in the number of edible insects living in tree bark, where these bugs are most easily reached with slightly longer beaks than is the average for this species. At the same time, there are fewer seeds to be had in the wake of this climate shift, seeds best broken up and consumed using shorter, sturdier beaks. The beaks will naturally vary in size within this bird population, and those birds with the longest beaks will be better suited for obtaining organisms from the tree bark. So, those birds will be more likely to survive and reproduce in this new climate situation than if they had shorter beaks. The next generation might then have slightly longer beaks on average, and if the climate situation continues, the process will repeat, resulting again in slightly longer beaks, on average, within the population.

On the other hand, birds that live in an environment with seeds hardened by drought might be best adapted with short, stout beaks. This is one of the most commonly cited examples of natural selection acting on random variation, often mentioned in biology textbooks. It nicely illustrates the basic idea of evolution by natural selection.

But notice that the variation is modest, and the beak sizes tend to wax and wane within a fixed range. So, while the example is one of the most commonly used to demonstrate natural selection, it is of only limited use in making a case for evolution by natural selection of fundamentally new animal forms from earlier ones.[4]

Microevolution and Macroevolution

MICROEVOLUTION REFERS to relatively modest evolutionary changes, like the ones mentioned above. Think of the way finch beaks vary in size, or how some bird species on windy islands without predators adapt to

1. Geospiza magnirostris.   2. Geospiza fortis.
3. Geospiza parvula.   4. Certhidea olivaȷea.

Figure 4.2. Drawings of Galápagos finches. Short, stout beaks better allow for eating hard seeds. Long beaks better allow for digging in tree bark to catch insects and other small organisms.

become flightless. That's microevolution. Macroevolution, in contrast, means evolutionary change that produces fundamentally new biological structures and forms of life. At some point in the history of life there were no bird wings. And then eventually there were. If evolutionary processes invented bird wings, that's macroevolution.

Entomologist Yuri Philiptschenko is said to have coined the German form of the terms "microevolution" and "macroevolution" in a 1927 German work.[5] The influential Russian-American evolutionary biologist Theodosius Dobzhansky introduced the terminology into English in his 1937 work *Genetics and the Origins of Species.* There he commented that "we are compelled at the present level of knowledge reluctantly to put a sign of equality between the mechanisms of macro- and microevolution."[6]

Why reluctantly? Because as Dobzhansky conceded, while we can directly observe and construct experiments that produce microevolution, we have not been able to observe or produce macroevolution. Even today when we attempt it, more than eighty years after Dobzhansky wrote those words, we continue to hit a microevolutionary wall, and quite early. We see this even in the case of microbes that reproduce rapidly and in enormous populations, where millions of mutations and tens of thousands of generations are possible.

So what "compelled" Dobzhansky to equate micro- and macroevolution? It seems that it was his commitment to the existence of macroevolution combined with the confessed lack of direct observational support for macroevolution. That is, he wanted to demonstrate that the entire diversity of life required no mechanisms beyond those of microevolution, but he couldn't observe or produce macroevolution in order to clinch the case, so he settled for demonstrating microevolution and then equating it with macroevolution.

Dobzhansky and other evolutionary theorists are, of course, free to equate the two, but the rest of us are free to note the crucial difference, the very inequality that Dobzhansky himself noted. Indeed, reason urges us to do so. Acknowledging the crucial difference, the inequality, is key to clear thinking on the issue.

Can unguided microevolutionary changes accumulate and lead to dramatic macroevolutionary changes? Can they, for instance, lead to the rise of the first ocean-going animals, or the first dinosaurs, or the first mammals? Can they produce sonar in bats? We cannot even rationally address the question until we first acknowledge the clear difference between microevolution and macroevolution.

Equivocation Alert

Equivocation is the logical fallacy of changing the meaning of a word in the middle of an argument. Take, for example, the following argument: "Whenever it's sunny out, the streets are dry. Harriet has a sunny disposition. Therefore, whenever Harriet is out, the streets are dry." The word "sunny" in the first place means the sun is shining; in the second place it means upbeat and cheerful.

Arguments defending evolution often resort to equivocation, trading on the fact that the term *evolution* can refer to several different things. Take, for instance, someone who says that evolution is a fact, where by "evolution" he means the idea that natural selection working on accidental genetic mutations has produced macroevolution, the evolution of new structures and forms in the history of life. Suppose that this person then tries to prove evolution in this sense by citing how breeders have bred different kinds of dogs—microevolution by artificial selection. So, at first evolution means macroevolution by natural selection, but then evolution refers to microevolution by artificial selection. The evolutionist has used a term in his argument in two different ways, but acts as if the meaning hasn't changed, or at least hasn't changed significantly. This is an example of the fallacy of equivocation.

We must understand that those who equivocate with the term "evolution" may not be acting in bad faith. They may not realize they are equivocating. But that doesn't mean one has to go along with their confusion. Instead, the next time someone asserts something about "evolution," press "pause" and ask what exactly the person means. And if the person points to evidence of evolution in action, ask yourself, what kind of evolution, if any, was just demonstrated? And does that evidence clinch the case for full-blown, unguided, microbe-to-man evolution? Does it contribute to the case but not clinch it? Is the provided evidence entirely beside the point? If so, what else, if anything, needs to be demonstrated to clinch the case for the full-blown theory of evolution?

A Competing Explanation

IN ASSESSING the claims for modern evolutionary theory, a worthy goal is to proceed as reasonably as possible, and to follow the evidence wherever it leads. Equivocating with the term evolution doesn't get us there. It produces fog and confusion when what we want is clarity and insight.

How can we proceed reasonably and in a way that's guided by the evidence? The science of biological origins is a historical science, and the historical sciences have developed a shared methodology for doing just this, proceeding reasonably and in a way that's guided by the evidence.

Historical sciences study clues in the present to solve mysteries about the past. In the historical sciences, investigators compare competing explanations for a given event or set of clues about a past event. Sometimes two or more explanations seem to adequately explain an event in question. If a decisive tie-breaking clue can be found, then one explanation can replace the other. If not, then it is not right for one explanation to declare itself "the truth" and anything else false.

Take an example from the historical science known as forensics, used to study crime scenes. A man is found dead in his home. Forensic scientists are called in to investigate and determine the cause of death. Death by some natural illness? By murder? By suicide? By accident? The man was found in his tub with evidence of a hard blow to the back of his head. One of the investigators concludes the man slipped and struck his head on the side of the tub. You can't very well hit the back of your own head hard enough to kill yourself, the investigator reasons. So clearly it was not suicide, he announces. Instead, it was death by accident.

But a second investigator points out that the man might have been struck in the back of the head by someone else. Maybe it wasn't an accident. The first investigator points to the blow to the back of the head and notes that the blow is perfectly consistent with his theory of an accidental fall. Case closed, he says. When the other investigator raises an eyebrow, the first investigator accuses the other of sensationalism, of preferring the most dramatic explanation, murder. There is no evidence of forced entry into the house, the first investigator further notes, and if every bathroom accident is to be attributed to some mystery murderer, where will the conspiracy theories end? No, he insists. He's going to write this up as a simple accident. The homeowner slipped, hit his head, and died. End of story.

Is that any way for a forensics expert to proceed? Of course not. He's failing to give due consideration to the murder hypothesis. Instead, he should acknowledge that there is an alternative explanation and that this is not an open-and-shut case. Further evidence is required to establish one view over the other.

The first investigator mentioned that there was no sign of a forced break-in. Good, but this is hardly decisive. The man could have been murdered by a friend or family member. Or maybe he left the front door unlocked. Instead of rushing to judgment, the first investigator should scour the scene more carefully for additional tie-breaking clues that might prove genuinely decisive one way or the other. If he did, he might find, for instance, a pewter bookend in the hallway that shows traces of having recently been cleaned with bleach, while the second bookend has not. The bookends also are shaped in a way that matches the wound on the back of the dead man's head. Important clues, but they won't even be considered if the first investigator has his way.

There is a case in origins biology not unlike the fictional scenario above. Similarities in genetics can be observed in various species. For instance, there is a set of genes involved in specifying the organization of the body as it develops. These are called Hox genes. We can see similarities in some Hox genes in species as disparate as fruit flies, octopuses, and humans. Evolutionary theorists assert that common ancestry is the explanation for these genetic similarities. That is, the similar genes are said to have passed from a common ancestor to these descendants, the various forms that share these common genes. Okay, that is one possible explanation for genetic similarities, but it isn't the only explanation.

Just as software developers reuse lines of computer code in different contexts as they design new software programs, or car designers reuse the principle of four wheels and two axles when designing a new car, so too might a designer of life have reused lines of genetic code across different species. This too is a potential explanation.

Indeed, computer scientist Winston Ewert argues that the pattern of similarities and differences in various genomes has more in common with the pattern of similarities and differences we find among the work of software designers, who reuse software modules in different contexts even as they build software programs with new elements and new arrangements of existing modules. Ewert suggests that this pattern of similarities and differences favors purposive design as the primary cause of the genetic programs that help code for the diversity of biological forms we find in the biosphere.[7]

Some evolutionary theorists, unfortunately, are like the first investigator above who dismissed the murder hypothesis by ruling it out as overly sensational, and then simply reiterated that his death-by-accidental-fall explanation was consistent with the blow on the back of the victim's head. These evolutionary theorists insist that inferring purposive design "isn't science" and behave as if common descent via unguided evolution is *the* explanation for genetic similarities, end of discussion.

Junk DNA or Junk Argument?

FORTUNATELY, SOME evolutionary theorists do a bit better than this. They argue that Darwinism's process of blind evolution by trial and error could be expected to produce a lot of genetic junk, and that our genomes are riddled with junk DNA. This, they say, is expected on evolutionary grounds but not if life were the work of an intelligence.

Francis Collins and Karl Giberson offer the example of a gene involved in synthesizing vitamin C. "Primates, including humans, require vitamin C in their diet, or they will suffer a disease called scurvy," they write. "What happened? The human genome has a degenerated copy of the gene that makes the enzyme for synthesizing vitamin C. This 'broken' gene has lost more than half of its coding sequence. To claim that the human genome was created by God independently, rather than having descended from a common ancestor, means God inserted a broken piece of DNA into our genomes. This is not remotely plausible."[8] Such a broken gene is called a "pseudogene."

There are, however, answers to this argument. Genetic errors could easily be from devolution over time. That is, an original design without these errors took on mutational errors in the course of numerous generations. While the replication process is extraordinarily accurate and even contains an astonishingly sophisticated error-correction system, it isn't wholly error-free, so we might expect errors to accumulate in some parts of the genome.

Also, because chimps and humans are similar in structure and function (they are both primates, after all), it is not unexpected that they would have a similar genetic sequence in a similar location. The fact that this gene ceased to work within the human lineage is not evidence for a common ancestor with chimps, let alone evidence for common ancestry instead of common design.

Also, the fact that our supposed pseudogene does not function for vitamin C production does not mean that it does not have any function. The version in humans could still have some as yet undiscovered function. The Darwinian paradigm has discouraged the search for further function in this and many other genes whose possible function has yet to be determined.

There is also the question why the remaining non-mutated portion is intact. If the gene were totally useless, why wouldn't the remainder of it eventually undergo further mutation or even be deleted from the genome? I suspect it does not undergo such mutation or deletion because that might be deleterious to the individual, decreasing her chance of survival—because the gene may serve a function. And therefore the unmutated portion remains, serving some still undetermined but necessary function.

Finally, if the evolutionary story that Collins, Giberson, and others tell were the case, we could expect to see this confirmed by the wider pattern of phylogenetic (evolutionary) relationships among the various animals found to lack the ability to synthesize vitamin C. But just the opposite is the case. As Sebastian J. Padayatty and Mark Levine, writing in the journal *Oral Diseases*, note, many of "those animals that lack vitamin C synthetic ability do not bear any phylogenetic relationship to each other, implying many independent mutations all resulting in the same phenotype. No common environmental influence is apparent. To date, there is no satisfactory evolutionary explanation for the apparent random loss of vitamin C synthetic ability."[9]

As for the vast sections of the genome that evolutionary theorists have deemed "junk DNA," there are developments that would seem to favor the design hypothesis over that of blind evolution. Design theorists predicted years ago that much of what evolution proponents designated as junk would turn out to have important functions,[10] and this design prediction has already proven true. Moreover, every year scientists uncover more evidence of the previously unknown functions of this so-called junk.

Ann Gauger, Ola Hössjer, and Colin Reeves comment that "pseudogenes have not received much attention in the scientific literature because they are assumed to be 'junk.'" But they say this is changing. "Where pseudogenes have been carefully studied, they are often found to be functional, and in some nonstandard ways," they write. "Part of the problem is that a pseudogene may be active in specific tissues only during particular stages of development, making identification of their functions difficult. Nonetheless, researchers in the field are confident that continued research will yield more evidence of functionality."[11]

Darwin's Test

BESIDES THE issue of genetic similarities and differences, there are other potentially tie-breaking clues worth considering, evidence that might point toward the work of a creative intellect and away from blind evolution. Let's look at one of these next, see how Darwinists respond, and consider how one might respond in turn.

In his *Origin of Species* Darwin offered a way to test and possibly even falsify his theory of evolution. "If it could be demonstrated that any complex organ existed which could not possibly have been formed by numerous, successive, slight modifications," he wrote, "my theory would absolutely break down."[12] With the development of high-powered microscopes and new observational techniques, we now know of many biological structures at the molecular level that can serve as candidates for potentially falsifying Darwin's theory. In the past few decades, numerous tiny biological structures have been discovered, intricate structures often referred to as *molecular machines*. Michael Behe, professor of biochemistry at Lehigh University, has argued that at least some of them could not have evolved in the way Darwin envisioned and therefore do falsify Darwinism. He suggests that a better explanation for their origin is purposive design; that is, a designing intellect fashioned them.

Central to Behe's argument is the idea of irreducible complexity. He defines irreducible complexity as "a single system composed of several well-matched, interacting parts that contribute to the basic function, wherein the removal of any one of the parts causes the system to effectively cease functioning."[13] If such molecular machines exist, how could they have evolved one small step at a time, given that they don't work until all of their many essential parts are in place? Behe argues that they couldn't have, and that molecular biology has turned up several irreducibly complex molecular machines, marvels of nano-technology that could not have evolved in the mindless, gradual way that Darwin and his successors envisioned.

To grasp the concept of irreducibly complexity, it helps to envision a familiar machine, the common mousetrap. It's relatively simple as far as machines go, but as Behe notes, it still requires "several well-matched interacting parts"[14] in order to function properly. If the hammer is removed, then the mouse will not be trapped. If the holding bar isn't there to hold the hammer back, then the trap will be closed all the time and won't catch anything. Take one of these essential parts away, reduce it by one key part, and it's no longer a functioning mousetrap. This is what Behe means by *irreducibly complex*.

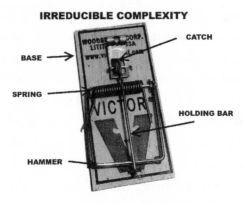

Figure 4.3. A mousetrap as an example of irreducible complexity.

The Little Engine That Could

Now LET's move from the relative simplicity of the mousetrap to examples from biology. Behe gives several in his book *Darwin's Black Box.*[15] These include the human blood-clotting system and light-sensing mechanisms in our eyes. But let's focus on his most famous example, a miniature motor that in some ways puts to shame even the motor of a winning Formula 1 racecar.

In an electron microscope the bacterial flagellum is a long whip-like tail extending off the jelly bean-shaped bacterium (Figure 4.4). But it's so much more. We now know that this whip-like flagellum functions as a motor, spinning many thousands of times per minute and moving the bacterium as a propeller moves a boat through the water.

Similar to a man-made machine, the motor component of the flagellum has a drive shaft attached to a rotor that turns within a stator and is anchored by bushings. Unlike a boat motor, however, it's fueled by hydrogen ions rather than gasoline.

Using advanced electron microscopes, biologists have been able not only to see the flagellum but also to learn about the tiny parts of this remarkable nano-machine. We can see some of them in the sketch below (Figure 4.5). Keep in mind that the actual flagellum is even more sophisticated than this simplified drawing suggests.

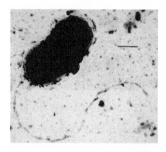

Figure 4.4. Electron micrograph of a bacterium. The large oval structure is the bacterium, and the long whip-like tail is the flagellum.

What does the bacterial flagellum have to do with evolutionary theory? For modern Darwinism to be true, this remarkable nano-machine had to have evolved through "numerous, successive, slight modifications," with no intelligence involved, only a series of small random mutations sifted by natural selection, over thousands or millions of generations.

Each mutational step has to be small because the odds are too great to produce big mutational improvements in a single big leap. (This is the standard view of neo-Darwinists.) In the same way that you could never randomly dump a box of Scrabble letters onto the board and expect

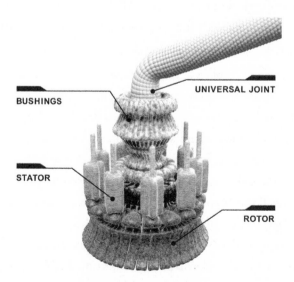

Figure 4.5. Depiction of the key components of the bacterial flagellar motor.

them to neatly spell out a completed game of interlocking English words, we cannot expect random genetic mutations to suddenly arrange DNA into the proper coding for the entire bacterial flagellum. No, taming the odds requires advancing in baby steps.

In addition, each of these baby steps on the evolutionary pathway must be functional to provide a selective advantage and get passed on to the next generation. It's not enough that the mutation will one day prove useful. Evolution doesn't look ahead. Evolution is blind. That's why the evolutionist Richard Dawkins called it "The Blind Watchmaker" in a book by that title. The process doesn't look ahead and think, "Hmmm, wouldn't it be handy for a bacterium to have a tail that can propel it. I think that over the course of many generations I'll locate and assemble a few dozen distinct, very specialized parts into a snazzy motor." No, evolution doesn't look ahead. It doesn't think. There's just a small random mutation in the DNA. Then the mutation either helps the organism or it doesn't. And it either gets passed on to another generation or it doesn't. Whether the mutation will one day be useful when assembled with various other possible mutations is of no concern to the evolutionary process. It doesn't care about the future. All that matters to it is whether a new mutation helps with function then and there, with survival and reproduction. It's blind to everything else.

Because of this, evolution requires a series of tiny, functional steps from simpler ancestor to fully outfitted flagellar motor. But there doesn't appear to be such a pathway to the bacterial flagellum. Instead, the evidence suggests that the entire structure must be present, with all the parts in place, for it to propel the bacterium. In this way it's just like the mousetrap. If it only has some of its several essential parts, it doesn't work as a flagellum. If one or more of these parts is a dud, or missing, the entire flagellum grinds to a halt. Or if all the parts are present and in good working order but haven't been precisely arranged, again, the flagellum doesn't work and instead just soaks up valuable resources from the bacterium, decreasing its likelihood for survival.

But of course the bacterial flagellum *does* work. How did such a technological marvel arise? Supporters of modern evolutionary theory have tried to provide a story as to how a series of lucky coincidences could evolve such a system. One idea they proffer is what's called co-option. That is, nature co-opts earlier simpler molecular machines on the way to creating the bacterial flagellum. This is a creative idea, to be sure, but even just in principle it faces a serious shortcoming. The parts on the simpler machines would have to be reworked to function in the bacterial flagellum and somehow all be fitted into place—just as a garage tinkerer would have to rework and carefully assemble scrap parts from old lawnmowers and such to build a motorized go-kart.

Evolutionists have proposed one possible precursor machine for the bacterial flagellum, a needle complex known as the type III secretory system (TTSS). Did the TTSS help pave the evolutionary pathway to the bacterial flagellum? The notion has several problems, as Scott Minnich and Stephen Meyer explain:

> This argument seems only superficially plausible in light of some of the findings presented in this paper. First, if anything, TTSSs generate more complications than solutions to this question. As shown here, possessing multiple TTSSs causes interference. If not segregated one or both systems are lost. Additionally, the other thirty proteins in the flagellar motor (that are not present in the TTSS) are unique to the motor and are not found in any other living system. From whence, then, were these protein parts co-opted? Also, even if all the protein parts were somehow available to make a flagellar motor during the evolution of life, the parts would need to be assembled in the correct temporal sequence similar to the way an automobile is assembled in factory. Yet, to choreograph the assembly of the parts of the flagellar motor, present-day bacteria need an elaborate system of genetic instructions as well as many other protein machines to time the expression of those assembly instructions. Arguably, this system is itself irreducibly complex. In any case, the co-option argument tacitly presupposes the need for the very thing it seeks to explain—a functionally interdependent system of proteins. Finally, phylogenetic analyses of the gene sequences suggest that

flagellar motor proteins arose first and those of the pump came later. In other words, if anything, the pump evolved from the motor, not the motor from the pump.[16]

Where does this leave us as regards the bacterial flagellum motor? So far, no one has proposed a reasonable step-by-step plan for how such a thing could have evolved. No one has even come close. So, as Behe notes, Darwin's theory has been put to Darwin's own test and failed.

The bacterial flagellum isn't alone, either. There are numerous complex systems for which no one has come even close to showing how they could have evolved through a series of slight, successive modifications. Indeed, evolutionists have not succeeded in providing a detailed, workable evolutionary pathway for any irreducibly complex biological system. Not one.

Hypothetical stories starved of evidence or detail are not adequate. Without a reasonable explanation for how such systems could have gradually evolved through purely natural mechanisms, modern evolutionary theory fails to explain a very significant part of what we see in biology and, indeed, fails one of its most basic tests.

Irreducible Complexity in Our Own Bodies

LET'S MOVE from tiny biological machines to large-scale systems in the human body that display irreducible complexity—in particular, the systems for transporting blood and carrying oxygen to the tissues. Such work requires the coordination of multiple structures and subsystems, all with extremely fine-tuned specifications. We need a heart and a series of blood vessels, making up the cardiovascular system. And we need lungs, airways, and muscles to bring air into the body—the respiratory system. The cardiovascular system's many essential parts must be in the correct location and arrangement for the system to work, and to get oxygen to the tissues it must perform an exquisitely complex dance with the respiratory system, which also needs its many essential parts in place.

There actually are many other subsystems that must be in place and working with these, but here we will focus on these two systems. They are crucial because the cells of your body need oxygen to keep them alive and functioning.[17]

The respiratory system contains lungs and airways as well as important muscles, including the diaphragm. When the diaphragm contracts, air is pulled into the lungs through the airways. The lungs, the airways, and the muscles must all work together for the respiratory system to function. But once the air enters the lungs, nothing would happen if oxygen couldn't get into the bloodstream. So there needs to be a precisely structured interface between the respiratory system and the cardiovascular system. Each system needs the other.

The tiny grape-like sacs in the lungs that receive air are called alveoli or alveolar sacs. The tiny blood vessels surrounding these sacs are called pulmonary capillaries. When blood first enters the lungs, it is low in oxygen and bluish in color. After absorbing oxygen, the blood turns red.

Together the alveolar sacs and capillaries form the interface by which the oxygen gets from the airways into the bloodstream. The walls of the alveoli and the walls of the capillaries have to be close together and incredibly thin for oxygen to diffuse efficiently. And there have to be a sufficient number of alveoli and capillaries for enough oxygen to diffuse. All these must be very precisely structured to work.

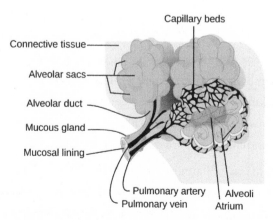

Figure 4.6. A highly simplified drawing of alveolar sacs and pulmonary capillaries.

Oxygen's Beast of Burden

YET EVEN with a complete cardiovascular system, a complete respiratory system, and a complete interface between them, there would still not be enough oxygen carried to the tissues. Why not? Because oxygen has very low solubility in the blood fluid (plasma), so the blood would not be able to absorb and transport sufficient oxygen to keep us alive. To get enough oxygen to the cells we need almost fifty times the amount of oxygen that naturally dissolves in the plasma.

This is a challenging biological engineering problem. What are the options for solving this problem? One option would be to enlarge each of these systems to absorb and carry more oxygen. Unfortunately, this would create a new problem because each part would have to be many times bigger. The heart would be bigger than the chest. And the lungs would be even larger. And where would all the blood vessels and the airways be located? There would not be enough room. Enlarged systems would not work. There needs to be a way to get fifty times more oxygen to dissolve in the blood without substantially enlarging the heart, lungs, and blood vessels. Even the smartest chemist might be stumped by this problem.

How was the problem solved? The answer is in a molecule called hemoglobin.

Hemoglobin is a protein and, as are all proteins, it is coded for with a twenty-character alphabet of amino acids. The comparison to language is illuminating but also in need of qualification. Amino acids may not function by symbolizing something else, in the way human words do, but are more akin to precisely specified parts in a sophisticated machine component. However, they are identical to software or text in English, in the sense that the choice and order of the "letters" are crucial.

Hemoglobin has 574 amino acids contained within four chains. As the letters in this paragraph are precisely selected and ordered to communicate information about hemoglobin, so the various amino acids are ordered within hemoglobin's four chains to give the molecule exactly the right shape and function. Hemoglobin, similar to thousands of other proteins, is an extremely complex and amazingly constructed entity, fine-tuned to carry out a crucial function. One molecule of hemoglobin can bind four oxygen molecules, hold onto them, and release them where and when they are needed. As many as 280 million hemoglobin molecules are found within one red blood cell.[18] There are about five trillion red blood cells per liter of blood, and approximately five liters of blood in the average adult human. By binding four oxygen molecules to each hemoglobin molecule, and by having so many hemoglobin molecules in a red blood cell, and so many cells in our blood, we are able to deliver enough oxygen to our tissues to stay alive.[19]

And proteins, keep in mind, often have very limited tolerance for error in their sequence of amino acids, with random mutations usually leading to diminished or lost function. Indeed, there is growing laboratory evidence that the specific and highly improbable sequence of amino acids that code for a particular fold (functional shape) of a protein can only tolerate a few alterations before losing function. For instance, one study reported on in *The Journal of Molecular Biology* made the case that if left to chance, the odds of a protein 153 amino acids in length having just the right sequence to fold and perform a specific function is about 1 in 10^{77}.[20] That's one chance in 1 followed by 77 zeroes. (More on those findings below.)

Putting It All Together

THE CARDIOVASCULAR system is an exquisitely orchestrated marvel, but unlike a marvelous orchestra, it is not merely diminished by the absence of one of its instruments—one of its subsystems. Instead, it would cease to work altogether. We need all of them present, all of them working, and all of them carefully coordinated to get oxygen in sufficient amounts to the numerous parts of our body.

No one has ever been able to offer a detailed account of how the cardiovascular system could have gradually evolved through blind natural forces. But even if a fully functional cardiovascular system could somehow have evolved in this way, it would still not be enough. Remember Darwin's challenge: "If it could be demonstrated that any complex organ existed which could not possibly have been formed by numerous, successive, slight, modifications, my theory would absolutely break down." What applies to a single organ applies equally to a system of interdependent organs, ones that cannot survive and function without the others. The system for providing oxygen to our cells requires the cardiovascular system with all its many essential parts, the respiratory system with all its many essential parts, the precisely structured interface between them, and the hemoglobin molecule with its special binding properties to be able to carry oxygen molecules in sufficient numbers.

None of these systems and subsystems are optional. Without all of them in place at the same time, we wouldn't be alive. So nature cannot evolve a few of the parts or subsystems at a time and wait around for countless generations while some of the other parts and subsystems evolve and come on line. Nature can't even wait around a single generation. It's do or die. Evolution, in this case, would need to proceed not by tiny steps but in a gargantuan creative leap, like dumping boxes and boxes of Scrabble letters on a table and somehow they spell out a series of interlocking English words that, in turn, spell out the unfolding sentences of an exquisitely ordered script for a multi-act play. There are less complex cardiovascular/respiratory systems in the biosphere, of course, but these have their own internal logic, and no one has been able to offer a detailed, functional evolutionary pathway moving from these relatively simpler systems (though still almost unimaginably sophisticated by human engineering standards) to a cardiovascular/respiratory system such as we possess.

Neutral Evolution

IN THE face of the irreducible complexity challenge, evolutionists have proposed other scenarios (in addition to the idea of co-option discussed above) to explain how such complex systems might have arisen by undirected, accidental processes. For example, some have argued that *neutral evolution* might help explain the origin of new biological functions. In simple terms, neutral evolution is based on the observation that some mutations in DNA are neither harmful nor helpful, but are neutral and don't seem to impact the organism in a significant way. As a result, natural selection would neither weed out nor select for these neutral mutations and, proponents claim, the mutations could continue to accumulate until at some later point they happen to join together in a lucky way to positively help the organism.

One of the most popular suggestions is that perhaps a gene could have been duplicated and one of the copies was "experimented on" through random neutral mutations while the other copy maintained the original function required for the organism to survive. Presumably the new copy would eventually acquire the more complex functional role and the old copy could then be eliminated.[21] It's certainly an interesting idea, but some problems with it have been identified:

1. Any step-by-step scenario that has been proposed is completely imaginary. The evidence is lacking to support the step-by-step evolution of the new system.

2. Neutral evolution avoids the problem of a given DNA sequence having to be functional at every step, but at a steep price. Now the process must build without natural selection to preserve beneficial changes. There is nothing in neutral evolution to lock in mutations that are building toward the completed sequence required by the system or subsystem in question. Remember, neutral evolution is said to happen where fitness considerations are mostly ignored, particularly as regards potentially helpful mutations. As a result, neutral evolution abandons natural selection in favor of random outcomes, i.e., luck. Yet chance is a poor candidate for building the kinds of irreducibly complex systems found throughout biology. As the required number of units in a sequence grows, the odds against it happening by chance quickly grow astronomical, becoming

essentially impossible long before the sequence is long enough to code for a functional system. So although neutral mutations might accumulate in an organism's DNA over time, those neutral mutations do not explain how new and sophisticated biological features arose.

3. There is a high energy cost for an organism to experiment with something that does not immediately produce a benefit. Evidence exists showing that some organisms will be quick to inactivate genes that have no adaptive/selective advantage.[22]

Like a Weasel

A PROPONENT of evolutionary theory might concede that this or that evolutionary scenario may have its shortcomings, but argue that at least we know that random point mutations in DNA can do impressive things at the level of individual genes and proteins. If that's the case, then surely evolution can gradually accumulate new lines of functional genetic code and, with those, new functions, features, organs, species, and ultimately, even whole new body plans. Let's consider the first half of this claim, since if modern evolutionary theory should work anywhere, it should be at the modest level of genes and individual proteins.

In the dance of molecular biological life, there are many different kinds of genes and many different kinds of proteins. In simplified terms, leaving RNA aside for now, let's assume that a gene is a stretch of DNA that can code for a given kind of protein.[23] The information content in DNA is based on the arrangement of the four letters (bases) in DNA. The letters are held in place by other molecules and organized into a special spiral called a double helix. The arrangement of the bases in DNA is comparable to the arrangement of letters in the sentences and paragraphs of this book, except that in the case of the English language there are twenty-six letters, while in DNA there are four letters (bases), typically abbreviated as A, T, G, and C. In both cases, it is the specific order of these letters that provides meaning or function. It isn't enough just to have all these DNA letters piled in. To function they have to be in a particular, functional sequence, in the same way that the letters of the sentences in an instruction manual have to be in some particular order to have meaning.

What is crucial about the information found in DNA? It is involved in specifying the arrangement or sequence of amino acids found in proteins, which were discussed a little earlier. Again, there are twenty different amino acids used in the synthesis of proteins. Connecting what was already said about proteins with DNA, the four-character alphabet found in DNA codes for the twenty-character amino acid alphabet. For instance, the hemoglobin molecule discussed above, which has 574 amino acids, has to have the right amino acid letters in the right order so that it will fold and function properly. The correct amino acid placed in the proper sequence depends, in part, on genes, and the information in the genes is based upon the ordering of the four DNA letters—A, T, G, and C.

In the previous century scientists deciphered the genetic code so that we now know how the cell takes the information in DNA (the sequence of the bases) and transforms it into a sequence of amino acids in proteins. The process is quite complicated.[24] But the main thing to know for our purposes here is that it is very precise. If the wrong base is inserted in the DNA, that mutational error can be passed on to the protein in the form of a mistaken amino acid. Just like a misspelling in a word, a genetic mutation can make a difference. A mistaken amino acid in a protein might cause the protein to fold incorrectly and not work as well, or at all.

Consider an illustration from human language. Let's take the simple sentence, "Methinks it is like a weasel," from Shakespeare's play *Hamlet*. What if it was mistakenly typed out as "Methinks it is like a weakel"? The final word in the sentence is no longer an English word. The sentence no longer makes sense. It's dysfunctional. In a similar way, we know that mutations can often cause serious problems for living organisms. For example, researchers have identified mutations in a protein involved in fruit fly reproduction that lead to a loss of proper function and, ultimately, premature death at either the pupal or larval stage. Several of these fatal results are caused by a single point mutation—the change of a single nucleotide "letter" in the DNA sequence.[25]

So it would seem obvious that mistakes are bad, right? Oddly, proponents of evolution believe that these same mistakes are the raw materials of evolutionary progress. At the most basic level they propose that these mistakes can lead to improvements in the protein.

Now, based on our everyday experience we might conclude that enormous ingenuity and forethought are required to build something like our oxygen transport system. Yet, according to evolutionary theory, it is all due to a series of useful mutational accidents in our DNA.

This is an extraordinary claim, but rather than dismiss it out of hand, we should see if there is any evidence that would count decisively in its favor. As it turns out, any such evidence is lacking, despite an extremely well-funded and assiduous effort by numerous scientists around the globe over several decades. There remains no detailed road map of how genetic mutations could lead to significant improvement and innovation. There is no documentation of these types of improvements in a step-by-step manner.[26] In the absence of such evidence a healthy skepticism is well warranted.

Supporters of modern evolutionary theory point to a few examples of proteins which, when damaged, provide an advantage under unique conditions. The few such examples that have been discovered, however, tend to be double-edged swords. For instance, a mistake in a protein might allow an organism to resist a particular disease, but that same damaged protein will generally not work as well in its normal function.[27]

One researcher, Douglas Axe, who worked in a lab at Cambridge, in England, calculated that the odds of producing a specific protein of 153 amino acids by chance are, as noted above, 1 in 10^{77} (that is 1 out of 1 followed by 77 zeros). To get any functional sequence of that length, the odds aren't much better, about 1 in 10^{74}. For every one functional se-

4. Irreducible Complexity and Evolution   / **113**

quence of that length, there are an enormously large number of gibberish sequences,[28] an enormous ocean of gibberish to swim around in hoping to randomly bump into the ultra-rare functional sequence that codes for a functional protein fold.

It's so enormous we need an illustration to even begin to get our minds around it. Our galaxy has roughly a hundred billion stars in it, and about 10^{67} atoms, so your odds are far better of picking the single winning atom, blindfolded and at random, from all the atoms in the Milky Way, than of nature stumbling by chance upon a single new functional protein fold from scratch.[29]

Also, in order to produce significant biological change, evolution has to stumble upon numerous functional protein sequences. And, in many cases, multiple proteins would have been required to work in coordination with each other to produce any biological function that could be subject to natural selection, such as the many protein complexes and molecular machines found throughout biology. Thus, even if Axe's experiment-based estimate is off by many orders of magnitude, the essential challenge to the Darwinian story remains: the odds of repeatedly stumbling upon functional changes and new forms amidst a sea of nonfunctional possibilities appear to be vanishingly small.

Inertia

WITH SUCH evidence against modern evolutionary theory, why do its proponents still hold to it? Answering such a question is, of course, largely conjectural, and motivations are unlikely to be exactly the same among even any two scientists, much less among all proponents of evolutionary theory. But speaking broadly, science is a thoroughly human enterprise, and human foibles get in the mix. Historians and philosophers of science have thoroughly documented that scientists, even highly successful ones, have tended to cling to their long-favored theories even in the face of mounting contrary evidence. As it has been said, change in science tends to come one funeral at a time.[30] This is especially the case in origins science where one is often dealing with inferences about unrepeatable past events rather than with a straightforward experiment that can be replicated in the lab. And it's even more the case when the theory in question, evolution, is regarded by some of its proponents as crucial for underwriting their worldview, namely the idea that there is no creator and that reality is ultimately nothing more than matter and energy.

So how do evolutionary theorists justify their support for the theory in the face of so much uncooperative evidence? Those among their number who acknowledge the problems raised above say they just need more time, that we should accept the theory of evolution while science searches for the missing evidence—that to do otherwise is "giving up on science."

It's understandable how they might feel this way, but it's not giving up on science; it's abandoning modern Darwinism—or more precisely, the idea that some cluster of purely blind evolutionary mechanisms could produce all the diversity of life we find around us. It's refusing to let a paradigm trump evidence. By all means, origins biology should continue to pursue promising research, including research into what evolutionary mechanisms can and cannot accomplish. But that is no justification to cling to an inference that has proven wholly inadequate to explain the origin of fundamentally new forms and information.

Uncommon Descent

Recall that modern evolutionary theory holds that life began with a single-celled organism that in turn evolved into other new forms, and so on until we get to the diversity of living forms we see around us. The idea is commonly illustrated by a gradually branching tree of life. But which forms branched from which ancestors? What did cats evolve from? Are bears and cats closely related? Distantly related? What did turtles evolve from? What about whales? You see, even if one assumes common descent of all living things, there remain thousands of questions about where particular species belong on the evolutionary tree of life. In trying to fill in these details, scientists use living and fossil forms, and they look for similar features across forms. The features used for comparison may be genetic, biochemical, or morphological.

They also make an assumption, namely that similarities often show evolutionary kinship. One could remain open to the possibility that a given similarity between two separate living forms was based on intentional design, in the same way that, for instance, wheels are found on many different kinds of vehicles, not because one evolved into the other but because wheels are a useful design strategy in a wide variety of contexts. But modern Darwinists rule the design possibility out of court and insist that similarities among different living forms cannot be explained as a common design strategy.

As a point of clarification, evolutionists do not assume that every similarity between species is due to a common ancestor that possessed that feature. Evolutionists make exceptions for what they call convergent evolution. These are cases where it is believed that the evolutionary process invented the common feature in question more than once in the history of life; for instance, the similar body forms of fish and dolphins, which are claimed to have evolved separately.

But generally, similarities are assumed to be caused by a shared ancestor that possessed the trait in question. And roughly speaking, the more similar two species are, the more recently their shared ancestor is thought to have lived. So, for instance, the most recent shared ancestor of bobcats and African lions is thought to have lived much more recently than the most recent shared ancestor of lions and bears.

The data sets for constructing an evolutionary tree are by their nature incomplete and subject to interpretation. That by itself isn't a fatal weakness in the argument for common descent by unguided evolution. There is, however, something that may be: radically different and contradictory evolutionary trees can be generated depending on which data sets are used.

When evolutionists construct evolutionary trees using the forms (the morphologies) of plants, animals, and microbes they end up with something quite different from what results when they construct an evolutionary tree based on comparisons of DNA sequences. Even the various trees based on DNA sequences often conflict with each other. Our genomes are huge and complicated, and to make the task of comparing things manageable, evolutionary biologists focus on one particular area of the genome and compare that part across different species. So one genetic evolutionary tree will be based on one part of the genome. A second on another. A third one on another. And so on. Each produces its own evolutionary tree, and these trees can contradict one another, often dramatically so.

Although many proponents of evolution still hold out hope of finding a consistent tree of life, that now seems unlikely. The trees are proliferating rather than beginning to converge on a single true tree of life.[31] To take just one dramatic example of the problem, and as bioengineer Matti Leisola and his co-author Jonathan Witt have noted, a 2013 paper published in the prestigious journal *Nature* "highlighted the extent of the problem. The authors compared 1,070 genes in twenty different yeasts and got 1,070 different trees."[32]

What are we to make of this proliferation of conflicting trees? If all life does indeed share a common ancestor, there is one and only one actual evolutionary tree. It's reasonable to see some conflict as scientists try to build ever more accurate means of discovering what the actual branching history of evolution was, but if evolutionary theory is true, we shouldn't expect to find this ever-expanding forest of conflicting trees. Such a trend makes better sense if the many diverse forms of life are not in fact related by common ancestry, but instead by common design. They could simply share some common design features because they made good design sense to their maker, much as cars, planes, and bicycles share many common design features even though none evolved blindly from the other.

Notice, by the way, that one doesn't have to take an extreme position here. It could be that intelligent design explains many of the recurring design themes we find in biology across different species, and that common ancestry explains commonalities among closely related species— the cat family, for example. That is, maybe all of the different cat varieties we find on Earth did in fact all descend from a single cat ancestor. But the evolution of all life from a single common ancestor through mindless natural processes? The comparative data cast a reasonable doubt on that idea.[33]

Final Thoughts

WHEN WE think about all the complicated structures found in living organisms, it boggles the mind. Many of these structures possess numerous essential parts, all of which must be present and in place for the system to function. This is known as irreducible complexity. In addition, many of these systems must work together with other irreducibly complex systems for the organism to survive—an irreducibly complex system of irreducibly complex systems. Not only are these coordinated systems consistent with intelligence, but their incredible sophistication also displays a level of genius that far exceeds that of the most brilliant team of human engineers alive. There is good evidence to conclude that unguided processes like those of Darwinian evolution could not produce even a small portion of one of these systems, let alone all of them in their complete and coordinated form.

Some have attempted to refute irreducible complexity by calling upon hypothetical processes like co-option or neutral evolution, or by pointing to some similarities between biological systems, but none of these responses identify a cause adequate to produce fundamentally new biological forms and information.

Others simply dismiss the problems. They say either that they have other evidence for evolution, or that evolutionists will eventually figure things out. Certainly science progresses slowly at times and patience is called for in the stately march of progress, but science often progresses by accumulating evidence against a reigning theory until the only reasonable strategy is to look for an alternative explanation that better fits the evidence.

Supporters of the modern form of Darwin's theory of evolution, neo-Darwinism, hold that natural selection acting on accidental genetic mutations can work creative marvels. But random mutations are, by and large, either neutral (having no observable effect) or damaging. The only caveat is that some damaging mutations do create niche advantages. Fascinating stuff, but it isn't evidence for blind evolution building novel forms and information. It's further evidence that the mutation/selection mechanism is, on its best days, capable only of very modest, degradative variations, like ripping the top off a sedan to create a makeshift convertible.

Those evolutionists who recognize the limitations of the mutation/ selection mechanism may still hold to evolution because of the evidence they see for common descent. But common descent is weaker than many suppose. The possession of common features in disparate species is only a strong argument for common descent if common design is ruled out of court from the beginning, prior to a consideration of the evidence. And the evolutionary tree of life that Darwin proposed remains curiously elusive, with various proposed trees jostling for the throne and many contradicting the others.

We are told that mainstream scientists overwhelmingly embrace modern evolutionary theory. But the truth of a scientific theory is not determined by majority vote. And indeed, the history of science is littered with now-discarded theories that were for a time held by the vast majority of scientists in the given field. Also, there are more than a few scientific dissenters from the theory, some of whom work, or have worked, at well-regarded and even prestigious scientific institutions, and who themselves have impressive records of scientific accomplishment.[34]

Given the growing challenges to modern evolutionary theory, perhaps it is time to put intelligent design back on the table of possible explanations and simply follow the evidence where it leads. It may well provide a new way forward toward a better understanding of the remarkable biological systems at the heart of life.

Review: Your Turn

1. What are some different meanings of the term *evolution?*

2. What evidence, if true, did Darwin acknowledge would seriously undermine his theory?

3. What is irreducible complexity? What is an example from the non-living world? What are some possible examples from biological organisms?

4. Even if we have a complete cardiovascular system, a complete respiratory system, and an interface between the two, what else is needed to ensure that sufficient oxygen is supplied to the body?

5. How have supporters of modern Darwinism tried to respond to evidence-based criticisms of the theory?

6. What are some of the evidential challenges to the idea of common descent?

5. BIOLOGY'S BIG BANG: THE CAMBRIAN EXPLOSION

Paul K. Chien

B Y NOW MANY PEOPLE HAVE HEARD OF THE TERMS "ANIMAL BIG Bang" or "Cambrian Explosion." These terms refer to the sudden, virtually simultaneous appearance of most of the major animal groups in the early part of the Cambrian period about 530 million years ago. Many people's first exposure to the concept came from the cover of *Time* magazine in December 1995. Boldly printed across the cover were the words "Evolution's Big Bang." The subtitle read, "New discoveries show that life as we know it began in an amazing biological frenzy that changed the planet almost overnight."

Evolution, according to mainstream theory, should be a slow, gradual process involving millions of accidental mutations and intermediate steps over a myriad of generations. How could terms such as "big bang," "explosion" and "amazing biological frenzy" describe such a plodding process? For many, both inside and outside the community of evolutionary scientists, it has sounded like a contradiction in terms.

Shortly after I saw the *Time* magazine cover story, a friend alerted me to two related articles in an official Chinese paper, *People's Daily*. One was entitled "Chengjiang Fossils Challenge Evolution" and used the term "Cambrian Explosion of Life." It was about an exciting Cambrian fossil find in Chengjiang County in Yunnan Province, located in southwestern China. The marine fossils there are so astonishingly well preserved that the location has been designated a World Heritage Site by the United Nations Educational, Scientific and Cultural Organization

(UNESCO).[1] The other article concluded that further study of these extraordinary marine fossils could prove a serious blow to traditional Darwinian theory.

I myself am Chinese, so now I was doubly intrigued. There was also this: the Cambrian fossils were marine fossils, and I am a professor of marine biology, so it's not hard to imagine how eager I was to study these Chengjiang fossils, firsthand if possible.

Body Plan Bonanza

ONE REMARKABLE thing about the Cambrian explosion generally, and the Chengjiang fossil find specifically, is the extraordinary diversity of animal forms. To convey what I mean exactly, I need to unpack the concept of body plans.

I taught marine biology at the University of San Francisco for some forty years, where I remain an emeritus professor; and one of my students' favorite off-campus activities was exploring tide pools along the rocky shores of the Pacific Ocean. At low tide, a multitude of intertidal animals were exposed, allowing my students to learn firsthand where the animals lived, what they ate, how they are adapted to their particular environment, how they reproduced, what their role was in the community, and much more. But before learning all that, my students were required to identify the animals by their scientific names: genus and species. For example, the scientific name of the most common California hermit crab is *Pagurus samuelis*. For some students, identifying the animals was a difficult task. Many closely related species look alike, especially in field conditions without the help of microscopes and without being able to dissect the specimens or use a proper reference key. But most students had little difficulty determining which major group each animal belonged to, even at first glance.

Why? Because these major groupings were based on highly distinct body plans, and the body plans were dramatically distinct one from another. Even when the students found a new animal they had never seen before, they could easily tell to which major group it belonged.

In scientific terms, these distinct animal body plan groupings are known as phyla. The division between phyla is highly distinct, and there are few, if any, intermediates between phyla. For example, the clams and mussels belong to the phylum Mollusca; the crabs and shrimp are grouped into the phylum Arthropoda; and most of the worms my students and I saw were in the phylum Annelida. To give you a sense of how broad and basic a phylum category can be, all mammals belong to the phylum Chordata, as do fish, amphibians, reptiles, birds, sea squirts, and lancelets. There is tremendous variety in there, but there are body plans so distinct from these body plans that they belong in a different phylum from Chordata, while the Chordata, for all their astonishing diversity, belong in the same phylum, due to the fact that they share certain very basic architectural features.

There are dozens of phyla, and according to standard evolutionary theory, these dramatically distinct body plans arose through a series of gradual changes over numerous generations, initially with only one ancestral species of a single phylum, slowly diversifying into two and then more. This process is understood as gradual and slow, one small mutational step at a time.

According to traditional evolutionary theory, all of biology started from an ill-defined single form called the last universal common ancestor, which evolved into two, then into more and more through time in a branching tree pattern as shown in many textbooks and museums. According to this model, the new forms develop from the bottom up, so to speak: one species evolves into two species... then a new genus... then a new family... and eventually there is enough difference among some of the forms that it makes sense to identify distinct phyla. Small differences followed by bigger differences followed by differences so large that there now exist forms with completely distinct body plans.

However, the pattern of the fossil record reported in *Time* magazine, the *People's Daily*, and later by others showed a pattern completely different from that of a slowly branching tree. According to present estimates, twenty of the thirty-three still living metazoan phyla, including seventeen of the twenty-seven living bilaterian animal phyla, appeared relatively suddenly in many places around the world during the Cambrian period—thus the labels "Cambrian Explosion" and "Animal Big Bang."

People's Daily mentioned that the rich fossil site in Chengjiang County was readily accessible from the city of Kunming in southwest China. Immediately I thought to myself how wonderful it would be to visit the fossil site someday and find out all about this enigmatic event. If I could, I would share the facts with my students and friends.

It was purely a passing thought. I doubted the Chinese government would grant an American access to the site, a crown jewel among the world's fossil sites, so I never believed for a minute that this dream could come true—and so soon.

Heading to the Field

Less than a month later, out of the blue, I was surprised and privileged to be asked to organize an international team of scholars to visit the fossil site and meet with the paleontologists who had made the big discovery. It turned out that these fossil experts were based at the Chinese Academy of Sciences in Nanjing, in the eastern part of the country and far from the fossil site. For me to organize such a complex group trip to Nanjing in eastern China and Chengjiang in western China proved a daunting task, even though I had several years of experience traveling in China on my own to teach biology in summer schools. International academic exchanges with China at this scale were not a common occurrence. However, with the generous help of many people and, later, the full cooperation of the Chinese scholars and the government, we made all the connections, solved all the financial issues, obtained all the neces-

Figure 5.1. Author Paul Chien in front of Maotian Shan (Mt. of
Heavenly Hat) near Chengjiang, China, during a later visit.

sary approvals, and waded through all the red tape, mostly by snail mail.
Five months after the invitation, our team arrived.

Our group included Professor James Valentine from the University
of California at Berkeley, and W. Y. Leung, chair of the Communication Department at the Chinese University of Hong Kong. Professor
Leung also convinced a famous television director from Hong Kong to
bring a small film crew along to record the visit. It was the first television
team outside of China to film the Chengjiang site. At that time, bringing in specialized camera equipment and filming in China required very
special permission. Looking back, it seemed like a miracle, and I still
wonder how so many closed doors were opened for us one after another,
and in such a timely fashion.

First stop on our trip was Nanjing. At the Chinese Academy of Sciences there, we received a very warm welcome from the director, and
met many scientists working in related fields. We also visited the labs of
two principal investigators, where we got our first glimpse of the oldest,

and extremely well-preserved, marine animal fossils of many different phyla. These creatures already exhibit bilateral symmetry, differentiated appendages and digestive tracts, and well-developed brains, as well as eyes. Valentine noted how the phyla and classes were fully developed when they first appeared in the Cambrian.

During this visit, the Chinese Academy of Sciences also arranged a full-day symposium about the fossils. In the morning, we heard talks from major researchers in the field, followed by a question-and-answer period. In the afternoon we were given a lot of time to exchange information and ideas about the explosion. Most interesting to me was the discussion on the possible causes of the sudden concurrent appearance of so many different animal body plans. Everyone seemed to agree that the explosive appearance of so many phyla without apparent ancestors contradicted the classic Darwinian model, both its original nineteenth-century form and the updated neo-Darwinian model developed in the wake of the twentieth-century revolution in genetics and molecular biology. The scientists and scholars realized that random genetic mutations acted upon by natural selection were not capable of generating so many disparate groups of animals in the short time available.

There was some disagreement on how long the Cambrian explosion took. The commonly cited time period in the literature is 20-30 million years, but some of the Chinese researchers seemed to think that the main thrust of the explosion took only 1-3 million years. The yellow shale layers containing most of the phyla were not very thick at all. Still others tried to explain away the seeming suddenness of the event. In any case, even assuming the wider window of time, and even though this seems like a long time to us, from the perspective of geology it is quite sudden for producing so many new phyla. The traditional Darwinian story simply did not fit with the fossil record, and new ideas and explanations were needed.

One of the Chinese scholars who spoke offered the common, still debated, idea that a sudden increase in the oxygen level in the ocean caused the explosion. Others theorized that perhaps the accumulation of nutrients in the ocean at that time, or shortly before, might have triggered bacterial and algal blooms that would in turn be a food source to feed a rapid development of animals. But while interesting, these explanations focus on *necessary* conditions for the Cambrian explosion (oxygen and a nutrient source), but do not offer a *sufficient* cause for the sudden emergence of all these animal body plans. It would be like claiming that because birds fly in the air, the existence of the Earth's atmosphere somehow caused birds to appear. Such explanations just don't make sense logically or practically.

A visitor to the meeting suggested another explanatory avenue: we could start comparing Hox genes in different animal groups. Similar Hox genes exist in many different species, and they help control the development of embryos. Slight changes in the Hox genes might have quickly given rise to different body plans, it was suggested. This was a new idea to many paleontologists at that time and seemed interesting, but where did the Hox genes come from in the first place? Later we learned that Hox genes often function as on/off switches of other coding genes or specify the positioning of various biological structures, but do not themselves transmit all the required biological information about body plans.

One scholar suggested that evolution might be a combination of chance and necessity working together, in that once a new body plan got established by chance, then by necessity it would radiate into different forms within the same body plan in the new environment. For example, when arthropods first showed up in the Cambrian period, a large number and variety of slightly different forms of arthropods immediately followed. However, arthropods seemed to be the only example; other phyla did not follow this pattern. Also, at best it would explain the rapid emergence of diversity within a phylum, not the sudden origin of so many distinct phyla in the first place.

The punctuated equilibrium model proffered by Stephen J. Gould and Niles Eldredge was brought up. On this model, species generally remain stable, showing little or no change over time in the fossil record, but when change occurs, it occurs rapidly in rare and isolated locations, leaving little record of the change in the fossil record. Punctuated equilibrium was based on the observation that species appear suddenly in the fossil record, but it does not provide an explanation of how the many body plans of the Cambrian could actually have arisen in the time available.

Thus it is that Sean B. Carroll, a mainstream evolutionary developmental biologist firmly committed to modern evolutionary theory, can state confidently, "The explosion of animal diversity in the Cambrian is one of the most important and compelling mysteries in the history of life." And he writes this in an endorsement of a relatively recent book on the Cambrian explosion widely regarded as a benchmark in the field and one that also emphasizes the persistent mystery of the dramatic transition from Precambrian sponges to the world of the Cambrian with its riot of animal body plans.

In that book, *The Cambrian Explosion*, authors Douglas Erwin and James Valentine remain committed to searching out a purely material evolutionary account of the Cambrian explosion, and yet they insist that this singular event in the history of life remains marked by important "unresolved questions," and they call the transition from sponges to the creatures of the Cambrian "the most enigmatic of any evolutionary transition in metazoans."[2]

The point is central enough that Christopher J. Lowe highlights it in his review of the book in the journal *Science*. "The grand puzzle of the Cambrian explosion surely must rank as one of the most important outstanding mysteries in evolutionary biology," he writes.[3]

Over the course of the symposium there was plenty of speculation, but no answers. The central question is what produced all those new body plans in a short period of time. No one seemed to have a good answer, and it felt like there was little progress. But I wasn't discouraged, because it struck me that here in a thoroughly academic setting the Cambrian event was being openly recognized as a unique "explosion" and a serious challenge to modern Darwinian theory, which was a big step forward for intellectual freedom of inquiry. Then, too, I knew that studies in Chengjiang had just begun; there was much to be learned and more data yet to be collected.

Chengjiang's Exquisite Cambrian Fossils

THE DISCUSSION at the symposium in Nanjing was fascinating, but for me it was only a prelude to what I most eagerly anticipated: our visit to the Chengjiang fossil site itself, arguably the best Cambrian fossil site in all the world. It did not disappoint.

Shortly after the symposium, we set out for the Chengjiang site with Chinese paleontologist J. Y. Chen and his colleagues, including Ms. Zhou, a highly respected paleontologist from the Nanjing Institute of Paleontology, who had a fossil, *Misszhouia*, named after her. Our journey began with a plane ride more than 1,000 miles across southern China to the southwestern city of Kunming. After departing from the plane, our group squeezed into a small car with all our gear, and after a nearly two-hour ride past villages and over the mountains, we settled into a quaint hotel nestled in the agriculture town of Chengjiang in the middle of tobacco fields. As we later explored our surroundings, I realized this hotel was the fanciest one in town.

Early the next morning, we took a short ride up the red rolling hills behind the town. The bouncing dirt road led us past a smoking phosphate mine processing facility and ended near a small quarry of loose yellow rocks, quite unremarkable in appearance. It looked just like several other hillsides in the region. Little did I know that this was the original site of one of the greatest discoveries of animal fossils—a place most paleontologists all over the world would love to visit.

We piled out of the vehicle and traipsed the short distance to the unassuming quarry. Ms. Zhou knew this place like the back of her hand. She skillfully wielded her geological axe a few times and cracked open some ordinary-looking yellow rocks. Suddenly an exquisitely preserved shrimp-like animal appeared in front of our eyes! Although the specimen was over 500 million years old, we could clearly see the fossilized image of its eyes, antennae, legs, and even the hairs on its legs. No wonder paleontologist Xian-Guang Hou once remarked that one of the Chengjiang fossils looked "as if it was alive on the wet surface of the mudstone."[4] I eagerly followed Ms. Zhou's lead and found half a dozen fossils myself in an hour. It seemed that everywhere we looked at the site we came across more of these exquisite, ancient fossils.

I want to share with you some photos of these remarkable fossils my colleagues and I have taken over the years. Some were taken on my first visit to Chengjiang.

One particular fossil fish, *Myllokunmingia fengjiaoa*, was discovered by Professor D. G. Shu and reported on in the journal *Nature*.[5] I was privileged to visit Dr. Shu's lab, and was thrilled when he took out this specimen and I was able to examine it in person under a light microscope.

The Chengjiang site is not the only Cambrian site to testify to the remarkable nature of the Cambrian explosion. For instance, the Burgess Shale in Canada (more on that remarkable fossil site below) also points to the abrupt appearance of many new phyla during the Cambrian. One of the more remarkable fossils from this Canadian site is *Metaspriggina*, a 500-million-year-old fish fossil (Lower–Middle Cambrian) showing a pair of well-developed eyes. There is little doubt that both invertebrate compound eyes and vertebrate camera eyes were already well developed early in the Cambrian era.[6]

Figure 5.2. *Stellostomites*, a disc-shaped, soft-bodied animal with a well-developed u-shaped gastrointestinal tract (the dark curved section at the lower right of center). Modern jellies belong to a different phylum and do not have this gastrointestinal tract.

Figure 5.3. Triangular structures surrounding the *Stellostomites* are conical shells of Hyoliths. Recent studies consider both as filter feeders related to other phyla, such as Phoronida and Brachiopoda, not sea jellies and mollusks.

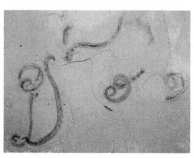

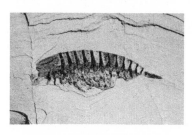

Figure 5.4. Worms from the species *Maotianshania cylindrica*.

Figure 5.5. The arthropod *Leanchoilia* is found in both the Chengjiang deposits, as well as the Burgess Shale in Canada.

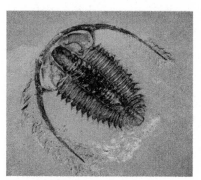

Figure 5.6. A well-preserved trilobite specimen from the Maotianshan Shale.

Figure 5.7. Hundreds of *Haikouella*, phylum Chordata, were found near the Chengjiang site in 1999.

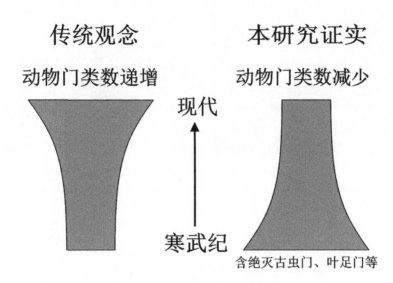

Figure 5.8. Recreation of a graphic provided by Professor Shu to the author, comparing the expected increase of phyla over time under the traditional evolutionary model (*left*) versus the actual data showing a large number of phyla originating in the Cambrian and a loss of some of those phyla over time (*right*).

Top Down vs. Bottom Up

ON ANOTHER trip, a few years after my initial trip, I took a television production team from Hong Kong to visit Professor D. G. Shu and his lab at North West University in Xian, China. He gave us his diagram comparing the traditional concept of the development of animal phyla with his own study and conclusion. The traditional model predicted that the number of animal phyla would gradually increase with time (left side drawing in Figure 5.8), beginning with a single or a few phyla. However, his research turned the traditional model upside down, showing that at the beginning of the Cambrian, most of the animal phyla appeared abruptly, and the number of Cambrian phyla decreased over time, by extinction (right side drawing). This pattern in the Cambrian fossil record may be as damaging to Darwinian theory as the sudden appearance of phyla.

Avoiding the Hard Facts

IN THE 1990s, before the Cambrian explosion data from the Chengji-ang fossil site was widely known, a museum in Golden Gate Park, San Francisco, featured an exhibit called the "Hard Facts Wall." On the wall, hard rocks containing fossil specimens were displayed and arranged in the pattern of a tree, as if the hard facts supported the idea that the history of life had followed a branching-tree pattern as predicted by Darwin.

There was just one problem. It wasn't true.

A trained geologist, John Wiester, was suspicious. Wiester, a member of the American Scientific Affiliation and its Committee for Integrity in Science Education, looked into the ages of the fossils on display and found that many of the fossils were not placed in the proper geological layers according to their age. Some of the older fossils were placed at the same level as younger fossils, while some of the younger fossils were placed in older geological layers. The overall history of these fossils could be fit into the pattern of Darwin's tree only by twisting the data.

Appalled, Wiester wrote an article entitled "Shell Games in California" showing that if the fossils had been arranged according to their true ages, they would show a pattern of parallel straight lines, with each line representing an animal phylum and the base of these isolated lines appearing abruptly at about the same time, around 550 million years ago.[7] In colloquial terms, this would be a "lawn model" rather than a tree model.

Wiester's analysis of the museum fossils gained corroborating support from what paleontologists were uncovering at Chengjiang. The data from this fossil site, released since 1995, substantiates this concept of a lawn model rather than a tree model. All the animal phyla there appear abruptly in the geological column, close together in time, and with no clear connections between them.

When I later learned of the Hard Facts Wall exhibit, I wondered why the museum staff would create an exhibit that was inconsistent with

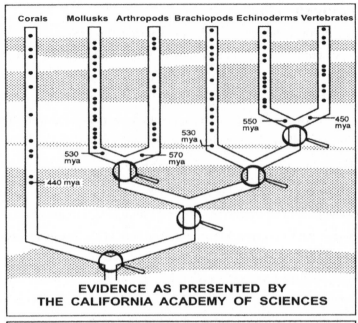

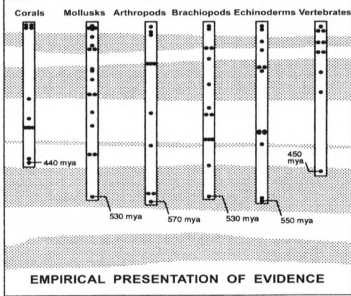

Figure 5.9. Representation of the Hard Facts Wall exhibit (*top*), and of the actual fossil data (*bottom*). Notice on the bottom the abrupt appearance and the lack of a branching tree pattern.

the actual data. The museum staff could perhaps be forgiven for not knowing about the Cambrian fossil discoveries in China that were starting to shake up the world of paleontology,[8] but why, I wondered, would the exhibit purposely misrepresent the ages of the various fossils just to make it look as if Darwin's prediction of a branching tree were true?

Another interesting feature on the original Hard Facts Wall was a series of large magnifying glasses placed over every branching point of the evolutionary tree. But, ironically, if viewers looked closely, under every magnifying glass, without exception, there were no fossils, just empty space. In other words, according to Darwin's theory, at each branching point there was supposed to be a common ancestor, but the museum did not, and could not, show any fossils of a common ancestor between two groups, and for a very simple reason: no such common ancestors had been found.

If museum visitors didn't look closely, the Hard Facts Wall looked like an impressive confirmation of Darwin's prediction. But to the trained eye, the Hard Facts Wall inadvertently demonstrated that the pattern of the fossil record contradicts that prediction.

Thankfully, this Hard Facts Wall exhibit did not survive when the museum reopened after a major renovation. On a new wall there was a display entitled "Timeline of Life on Earth," showing major events starting 4.6 billion years ago when the Earth was formed and continuing to the later start of life on Earth and onwards.

In two separate visits soon after the renovation, I looked to see how they would show the Cambrian explosion, which by that time was much better known in the scientific literature. Unfortunately, it turned out that the most important discovery in paleontology of the twentieth century was completely missing. The major events shown on the museum wall jumped from 650 million to 450 million years ago, completely skipping the Cambrian explosion! Again, I wondered why the museum would omit this critical piece of evidence that challenged Darwin. I still wonder if this evidence will eventually be included.

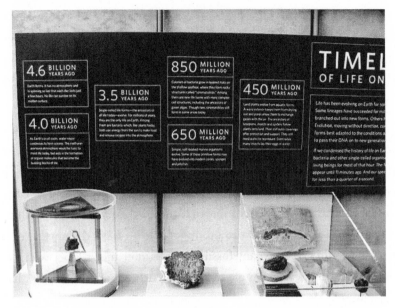

Figure 5.10. California Academy of Sciences museum display of the "Timeline of Life on Earth," missing one of the most important discoveries of the twentieth century in biology: the Cambrian Explosion, approximately 530 million years ago.

Beijing National Museum of Natural History

I HAD another, more positive, museum experience halfway around the world. Several years after my first visit to Chengjiang, I visited the National Museum of Natural History in Beijing. To my pleasant surprise, I found a large room housing an exhibit called the "Cambrian Big Bang of Life." A beautiful collection of Chengjiang fossils were on display. In the summary diagram, the museum showed a lawn model to illustrate the development of animal phyla since the early Cambrian period, instead of the textbook standard Darwinian tree model. The Beijing diagram was much more consistent with the actual fossil record.

In the Beijing diagram, vertical solid parallel yellow lines were used to represent the history of animal phyla. The phyla were correctly depicted with most of them beginning in the early Cambrian, and the parallel lines with no interconnections between them showed that there was no known evolutionary relationship between the phyla since that

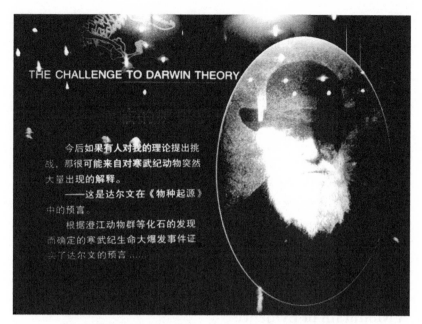

Figure 5.11. Panel from a fossil exhibit at the Beijing National
Museum of Natural History, noting the challenge to Darwin's
theory posed by the Cambrian fossils at Chengjiang.

time. Only the solid lines for the sponges and mollusks extended earlier
into the late pre-Cambrian (reflecting that sponge and mollusk fossils
had been found predating the other phyla), and the other phyla had only
dotted lines before the Cambrian, raising the question of whether they
had an earlier origin. It was gratifying to see that the Beijing exhibit was
much more accurate than the San Francisco museum's exhibit, showing
the actual data rather than trying to uphold the Darwinian tree model
in the face of contrary evidence.

Perhaps more remarkable was the concluding panel of the Beijing
exhibit, quoting a concern Darwin himself had raised in *The Origin of
Species*. Darwin acknowledged that the sudden appearance of a large
number of animals during the Cambrian period might challenge his theory. The last panel of this museum display concluded by observing that
the discovery of the Chengjiang fauna and other fossils had confirmed

the reality of the Cambrian Explosion, confirming Darwin's concern and underscoring the challenge to his theory.

I was grateful for the remarkable opportunity I had received several years earlier to visit Chengjiang and see firsthand in the field the fossils that challenge Darwin's theory. The Beijing exhibit gave me hope that perhaps more people would start to learn the truth about the fossil record.

Reflecting on these two very different museum experiences, I am reminded of the ironic observation made by Chinese paleontologist J. Y. Chen when answering questions after a lecture he gave in the United States on one of his visits: "In China, we can criticize Darwin, but not the government. In America, you can criticize the government, but not Darwin."[9]

A Mountain of Evidence

A FEW years later, in the early 2000s, I was privileged to participate in another discussion about the cause of the Cambrian explosion, this time on a mountaintop in southwestern Canada.

Several Canadian geologists, along with researchers from Discovery Institute's Center for Science and Culture, invited me to join them on a special guided hike up Wapta Mountain in Canada's Yoho National Park to visit the Burgess Shale, the most famous Cambrian fossil site in the western world. This site was discovered in 1909 by Charles Walcott, secretary of the Smithsonian Institution of the United States. This was the site all Chinese paleontologists I knew would consider an honor to visit. To me, the opportunity was the chance of a lifetime, and I happily accepted the invitation without hesitation.

Our group met in a small parking lot at the base of the mountain on a sunny day in July. It took us more than four hours to make the hike. We needed to stop and rest often, especially on the last stretch. At some points the trail seemed to go straight up (not actually, but it felt like it!) and the air was thin.

When I finally reached the site of the Burgess Shale, I looked around at the surrounding snow-covered mountains, glaciers across the valley, and the quarry right beside me, trying to imagine how Walcott and others worked there a century ago.

For visitors now, it is prohibited to collect fossils or even any rock samples at the site, but we could turn over loose rocks left by previous workers. I found a variety of partly broken marine invertebrate fossils scattered around. I could recognize many well-preserved arthropods, worms, sea jellies, and brachiopods. Most of them were similar to those I had seen in China, but there were a few unique fossil species I had not seen before. However, they all belonged to the same set of body plans present in both locations.

Our guide, who held two PhDs in related fields, gave an excellent introduction to the history of discovery and studies since Walcott. He opened a steel lockbox kept at the site, brought out a wonderful collection of exquisite fossils representing many phyla, and gave an interesting talk on each of them. In his concluding remarks, he praised the wonderful process of evolution for producing such a rich treasure millions of years ago and stated that without evolution there would be no humans now.

The youngest member of our group, a teenager, asked our official guide a very simple question: "Where did all the new DNA come from?"—meaning that an explosive appearance of very different body plans and different kinds of organisms must need a significant amount of new DNA to code for them. Where did such diverse sets of new DNA come from in this explosive event?

Our guide had seemingly never thought of this question before, as he hesitated for a few seconds and finally acknowledged, "That is a very good question." It seemed to me that he had decided that evolution must somehow have produced all the new DNA, and that he had decided this without even considering how this could have occurred. Hopefully the honest question of an inquisitive teenager gave our guide something to think about in the days after our visit.

Cambrian Quagmire

HAVING REFLECTED on the many discussions about the potential causes of the Cambrian explosion, both in the scientific literature and in conversations that I have participated in stretching back to my initial trip overseas to visit to the Chengjiang fossil site twenty years ago, it strikes me that not much progress has been made along traditional lines. Most people are still bogged down in some form of the Darwinian framework even though the fossil record suggests something quite different.

Some do try to think outside the traditional box. In November of 2016, many distinguished biologists and scientists met at a conference hosted by the Royal Society of London, one of the most distinguished scientific organizations in the world. A key area under discussion was the growing dissatisfaction with the neo-Darwinian explanation for the generation of biological novelty.

Two years later, an announcement for a conference held in Salzburg, Austria, was even more direct in its critique of neo-Darwinism: "For more than half a century it has been accepted that new genetic information is mostly derived from random, error-based events," the announcement read. "Now it is recognized that errors cannot explain genetic novelty and complexity."[10]

What sort of progress have evolutionists made in coming up with a purely materialistic alternative to modern Darwinism for the Cambrian explosion? The situation has become so desperate that recently several scientists from different fields joined together to propose that the Cambrian animals, as well as the first life on Earth, came from outer space.[11] There is precious little evidence for this extra-terrestrial theory. I see this kind of proposal as an admission of how existing evolutionary explanations for the Cambrian explosion, Darwinian and otherwise, have failed.

In contrast to these proposals, which try to provide a purely natural-istic explanation for the explosion of life in the Cambrian, philosopher of science Stephen Meyer and others have proposed intelligent design as the best explanation. The idea certainly fits the fossil data much better than does traditional evolutionary models.[12]

My Study of the Precambrian Sponge Embryos

FINALLY, I want to share with you my own experience studying some of the remarkable early life forms on Earth, and briefly explore the light it sheds on the question of animal origins.

During my studies as a graduate student in the 1960s, I learned techniques to study the structure of living animal tissues and cells using electron microscopes. Mastering these techniques turned out to be very useful when applied to minute specimens in rocks.

Years later, as I was cooperating with scholars from different parts of China, we found large numbers of nearly perfectly spherical objects in 570-million-year-old phosphorus-rich rocks from Guizhou province, China, just east of Kunming City. This is from the period just before the Cambrian layers. The rock samples were cut into half-inch slices and glued onto microscopic glass slides. Then the rock slices on the glass were carefully ground by hand down to wafer-thin so that we could study them through light microscopes.

In many of the thin rock slides, we found many microscopic round fossilized objects. Some of these spheres were algal cell fossils. These were easy to identify by their thick cell walls and daughter cells that tend to adhere together, sharing a common cell wall as they divide. But a large percentage of the spheres appeared to be the fossils of sponge cells and embryos with characteristic spicules. (No other known group of animals contains spicules.) The sponge eggs and early embryos were in the range of 0.6 to 0.7 mm in diameter. In 1999, we presented our findings at a scientific conference in Kunming, China, sponsored by the Early Life Research Center and the Chinese Academy of Sciences.[13]

My techniques in scanning electron microscopy came in handy in later research. In those further studies, I photographed these sponge eggs and early embryos at much higher resolutions. After carefully cracking them open and using a scanning electron microscope, I could identify cellular structures inside the cells, such as the nuclei and granules of egg yolk, that light microscopy could not resolve. In 2001, my colleagues and I presented another paper illustrated with scanning electron micrographs at a conference at the University of California, Berkeley, detailing our discoveries.[14]

During this work I was amazed by the discoveries we made, but as I look back now after more than a decade, I find that I am even more amazed by what we didn't see. When my colleagues and I searched through thousands of 570-million-year-old thin slides of Precambrian rock samples and photographed thousands of isolated objects under a scanning electron microscope, we found only sponges and algae, and no forms of life that even approached what one might deem bilaterian animals. The humble sponges were as close as it came, and even the identification of Doushantou/Weng'an fossils as sponge embryos has recently been disputed.[15]

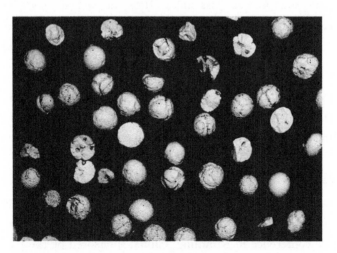

Figure 5.12. Electron microscope image of 570-million-year-old small round fossils of sponge specimens and algae.

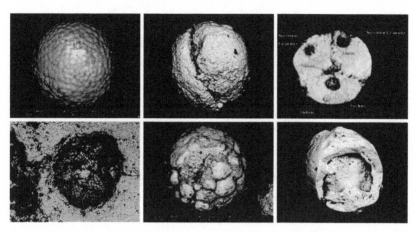

Figure 5.13. *Top left*: Well-preserved fossil of sponge egg cell with the outer membrane intact. *Top center*: Fossil of sponge embryo at the two-cell stage with the outer membranes removed. *Top right*: Fossil of sponge embryo cracked open showing cellular content of three cells. *Bottom left*: Enlarged and rotated image of the same fossilized embryo, showing the round nucleus in three dimensions at the center of the cell. *Bottom center*: Embryo stage where more than thirty cells can be counted. *Bottom right*: Fossilized sponge embryo at a more advanced stage of development.

My understanding is that scientists and their students at several labs in China have also studied those Precambrian rocks and confirmed our discoveries of sponge eggs and embryos. Adult sponge body fossils were also reported. Some evolutionists were hoping to find more animal remains that could be claimed as Cambrian precursors. So far, the rocks refuse to yield the evidence these researchers were hoping for. The problem is exacerbated by the fact that evolutionary theory predicts countless missing links between sponges (or some still earlier, simpler life form) and the Cambrian animal phyla. The theory needs countless transitionals, but continues to go begging for even a very few.

Some have tried to rescue evolutionary theory by claiming that there might have been many precursor animals leading up to the Cambrian, and it's just that Precambrian conditions were not very good at preserving those fossils, so those precursors are missing from the fossil record. But if the conditions for fossil preservation were so poor, why did they manage to preserve soft, delicate sponge eggs and early embryos, and preserve them extremely well, including the nucleus in eggs and embryo cells? Given this, why have no precursors to the Cambrian animals yet been found?

Alternately, if—as a few Precambrian fossil specialists have suggested—the Doushantou/Weng'an fossils are not sponge embryos, then one might again try to argue that the Cambrian explosion is merely an artifact of an incomplete fossil record. But any attempt to dismiss the Cambrian explosion as mere illusion, with or without Precambrian sponge embryos, flies in the face of mounting evidence.

As German paleontologist Günter Bechly notes,[16] vast fossil troves of Ediacaran-age fossils have recently been discovered in Mongolia and China,[17] and these sites lack any bilaterian animals and have only yielded fossil algae. The fact that these rocks preserve soft-bodied fossils like algae is significant because these localities are of the Burgess Shale type, which shows that the preservation conditions were capable of preserving small, soft-bodied organisms—exactly the type of creatures that are proposed to be the ancestors of Cambrian animals. The fact that they do not preserve anything that resembles such animal ancestors indicates that those animals were simply not present. Even a recent paper in *PNAS* that tried to downplay the Cambrian explosion acknowledged that these new sites show that animals are unknown from the Ediacaran not because of preservational issues, but because they definitely did not yet exist.[18]

What of those who interpret certain trace fossils as suggesting possible animal forms in the Precambrian, thus partially mitigating the astonishing efflorescence of new animal body plans in the Cambrian? "The Ediacaran record falls far short of establishing the existence of the wide variety of transitional intermediates that a Darwinian view of life's history requires," Meyer comments. "The Cambrian explosion attests to the first appearance of organisms representing at least twenty phyla and many more subphyla and classes, each manifesting distinctive body plans. In a best case, the Ediacaran forms represent possible ancestors for, at most, four distinct Cambrian body plans, even counting those documented only by trace fossils. This leaves the vast majority of the Cambrian phyla with no apparent ancestors in the Precambrian rocks."[19] Further, the majority of alleged animal trace fossils from the Ediacaran has been refuted by a recent experimental study, which exactly reproduced all these traces as artifacts of stirred up bacterial mats.[20]

And as we saw at the beginning of this chapter, it isn't just Meyer and other design theorists. Indeed, that the Cambrian explosion was a real event is the mainstream view of Cambrian paleontologists. As Erwin and Valentine emphasize, "Several lines of evidence are consistent with the reality of the Cambrian explosion."[21] Or as observed by Martin Scheffer, a Dutch ecologist, winner of the Spinoza Prize, and a member of the US National Academy of Sciences, "It could be that earlier rocks were not as good for preserving fossils," but we now know that "well preserved fossils do exist from earlier periods, and it is now generally accepted that the Cambrian explosion was real."[22]

Listening to the Whispers of the Past

Darwin recognized that the fossil record posed a serious difficulty for his theory. He hoped that future discoveries would overturn the picture and confirm his prediction of a slow, gradual, step-by-step evolutionary process, complete with a fossil record that looked like a branching tree. However, since Darwin's time the fossil record has stubbornly refused to confirm his prediction. Instead, as we have discovered more—including the remarkable fossils sites in China and Canada testifying to the astonishing diversity and suddenness of the Cambrian explosion—matters have only gotten worse for Darwin's story.

What are we to do with these findings? Rather than pretending Darwin's tree is still healthy, rather than hiding data or presenting a one-sided picture for museum attendees, we need to find the courage to accept the fossil record for what it is, including the fascinating record of the abrupt appearance of numerous animal phyla during the Cambrian in an explosive burst of creativity. Then we need to follow this evidence, this insistent pattern, to the best explanation. I submit to you that the best explanation invokes the only cause with the demonstrated ability to generate new biological form and information so quickly. It is the one cause known to create in a top-down pattern such as we find in the fossil record. That cause is intelligence.

Review: Your Turn

1. Where did Paul Chien go to see fossils from the Cambrian period?
2. Why do scientists refer to a "Cambrian Explosion?" What is it about the appearance of these animals on the Earth that is like an "explosion" or a "Big Bang"?
3. What is it about the Cambrian Explosion that challenges Darwin's theory of evolution?
4. Why do you think the San Francisco museum exhibit placed the fossils in the shape of a tree, with some fossils in the wrong place on the timeline?
5. How was the Beijing museum's exhibit different from the San Francisco museum's exhibit?
6. Why is it significant that so many soft-bodied sponge and sponge embryo fossils have been preserved right before the time of the Cambrian Explosion?

ENDNOTES

INTRODUCTION

1. The picture of electrons orbiting around the nucleus of the atom in the way planets orbit around a host star is best viewed as a useful stepping stone—both in the history of chemistry and for beginning chemistry students—rather than as a rigorous way of understanding the atom. Physicists and chemists now think of electrons as existing in a sort of "cloud" around the atom, where their location and motion are described by probabilistic considerations, quite different from Newtonian planetary mechanics.

2. Photograph, Einstein with Edwin Hubble and Walter Adams at Mt. Wilson Observatory, January 1931, California Institute of Technology Archives, http://archives-dc.library.caltech.edu/islandora/object/ct1%3A8407.

3. Arno Penzias, "Creation Is Supported by All the Data So Far," in *Cosmos, Bios, Theos*, eds. Henry Margenau and Roy Abraham Varghese (La Salle, IL: Open Court Press, 1992), 83.

4. Claude Shannon, "A Mathematical Theory of Communication," *Bell System Technical Journal* 27 (1948): 379–423, 623–56. In the following year, this article was published in book form as Claude Shannon and Warren Weaver, *The Mathematical Theory of Communication* (Urbana: University of Illinois Press, 1949).

5. J. D. Watson and F. H. Crick, "Molecular Structure of Nucleic Acids: A Structure for Deoxyribose Nucleic Acid," *Nature* 171 (1953): 737–8.

6. See Michael A. Flannery, *Nature's Prophet: Alfred Russel Wallace and His Evolution from Natural Selection to Natural Theology* (Tuscaloosa, AL: University of Alabama Press, 2018), chap. 1 and 3.

7. Flannery, *Nature's Prophet*, 113–19.

8. Stephen Jay Gould, "Abscheulich! (Atrocious!): Haeckel's Distortions Did Not Help Darwin," *Natural History* 109, no. 2 (March 2000): 42–9.

9. Elizabeth Pennisi, "Haeckel's Embryos: Fraud Rediscovered," *Science* 277, no. 5331 (September 5, 1997): 1435.

10. See Karen L. Wellner, "Lessons from Embryos: Haeckel's Embryo Drawings, Evolution, and Secondary Biology Textbooks" (PhD diss., Arizona State University, 2014), https://repository.asu.edu/attachments/134940/content/Wellner_asu_0010E_13836.pdf. For a more in-depth exploration of the issue, see Jonathan Wells, *Icons of Evolution: Science or Myth? Why Much of What We Teach About Evolution Is Wrong* (Washington, DC: Regnery, 2000) and *Zombie Science: More Icons of Evolution* (Seattle: Discovery Institute Press, 2017). Wells's website, https://iconsofevolution.com, also has short videos highlighting the persistent textbook problems.

11. Gerd B. Müller, "Why an Extended Evolutionary Synthesis Is Necessary," *Interface Focus* (August 18, 2017), https://doi.org/10.1098/rsfs.2017.0015. It should be noted that Müller, while open to expanding modern evolutionary theory's explanatory toolkit, hews to the dictates of methodological materialism.

12. See artist's rendition of the bacterial flagellum and an electron micrograph of the flagellar motor at https://classconnection.s3.amazonaws.com/114/flashcards/717114/jpg/flagella1318232583699.jpg.

1. THE BIG BANG AND THE FINE-TUNED UNIVERSE

1. Cosmologists continue to refine their understanding of the age of the universe, and some recent findings suggest that the current estimate of 13.8 billion years may need to be revised. However, whether or not new studies and measurements end up changing our best estimate of the exact age of the universe, the key point, as discussed later in this chapter, is the fact that the universe is finite in age, and thus had a beginning.

2. Guillermo Gonzalez and Jay W. Richards, *The Privileged Planet: How Our Place in the Cosmos is Designed for Discovery* (Washington, DC: Regnery Publishing, 2004), 171.

3. Luke Mastin, "The Expanding Universe and Hubble's Law," The Physics of the Universe, accessed November 1, 2019, https://www.physicsoftheuniverse.com/topics_bigbang_expanding.html. Recent research has revived the cosmological constant, but its precise value does not make for a static universe, as Einstein had hoped. Evidence for an expanding universe is stronger than ever. Indeed, the expansion rate of the universe appears even to be accelerating. In any event, the key takeaway from Einstein's experience is that his preconceptions and commitments led him to explain away, rather than follow, the evidence.

4. Luke Mastin, "Georges Lemaître (1894–1966)," The Physics of the Universe, accessed November 1, 2019, https://www.physicsoftheuniverse.com/scientists_lemaitre.html.

5. Georges Lemaître, quoted in George Gamow, *The Creation of the Universe* [1952] (New York: Dover, 2004), 51.

6. Arthur S. Eddington, "The End of the World: From the Standpoint of Mathematical Physics," *Nature* 127 (March 21, 1931): 447–53, https://doi.org/10.1038/127447a0.

7. Helge Kragh, "Big Bang: The Etymology of a Name," *Astronomy & Geophysics* 54, no. 2 (April 1, 2013): 2.28–2.30, https://doi.org/10.1093/astrogeo/att035.

8. Alaina G. Levine, "The Large Horn Antenna and the Discovery of Cosmic Microwave Background Radiation," American Physical Society, 2009, https://www.aps.org/programs/outreach/history/historicsites/penziaswilson.cfm.

9. Nicholos Wethington, "The Switch to Digital Switches off Big Bang TV Signal," Universe Today, February 16, 2009, https://www.universetoday.com/25560/the-switch-to-digital-switches-off-big-bang-tv-signal/.

10. "6 Things You May Not Know about the Afterglow of the Big Bang," Physics.org, accessed November 1, 2019, http://www.physics.org/featuredetail.asp?id=45.

11. *A Short History of the Universe*, episode 3, "The Photon Epoch," Highbrow Learning Inc., accessed November 1, 2019, https://gohighbrow.com/the-photon-epoch/.

12. See a brief video about the Cosmic Microwave Background Radiation at Piled Higher and Deeper, "Cosmic Inflation Explained," YouTube, video, 3:42, July 22, 2014, https://www.youtube.com/watch?v=_llA2q1rlSg.

13. Martin White, "The Cosmic Rosetta Stone," *Martin White* (personal web page), University of California Berkeley, Department of Astronomy, November 1997, accessed November 1, 2019, http://w.astro.berkeley.edu/~mwhite/rosetta/.

14. Karl Tate, "Cosmic Microwave Background: Big Bang Relic Explained (Infographic)," Space.com, April 3, 2013, https://www.space.com/20330-cosmic-microwave-background-explained-infographic.html.

15. William Lane Craig, "The *Kalam* Cosmological Argument," Reasonable Faith, 2015, https://www.reasonablefaith.org/writings/popular-writings/existence-nature-of-god/the-kalam-cosmological-argument/.

16. Alexander Vilenkin, *Many Worlds in One: The Search for Other Universes* (New York: Hill and Wang, 2006), 176. His analysis rules out various attempts to postulate a beginningless universe, including the idea that the universe has expanded and contracted eternally, in an endless series of Big Bangs and Big Crunches. As he and co-author Audrey Mithani concluded in a 2012 paper, "All the evidence we have says that the universe had a beginning." Audrey Mithani and Alexander Vilenkin, "Did the Universe Have a Beginning?" arXiv.org, April 20, 2012, https://arxiv.org/pdf/1204.4658.pdf. See also a *New Scientist* article about his conclusions by Lisa Grossman, "Why Physicists Can't Avoid a Creation Event," *New Scientist*, January 11, 2012, https://www.newscientist.com/article/mg21328474-400-why-physicists-cant-avoid-a-creation-event/.

17. Anil Ananthaswamy, "Is the Universe Fine-Tuned for Life?," *NOVA*, PBS Online, March 7, 2012, http://www.pbs.org/wgbh/nova/blogs/physics/2012/03/is-the-universe-fine-tuned-for-life/.

18. Carl R. Nave, "Fundamental Forces," HyperPhysics, accessed November 1, 2019, http://hyperphysics.phy-astr.gsu.edu/hbase/Forces/funfor.html.

19. Geraint F. Lewis and Luke A. Barnes, *A Fortunate Universe: Life in a Finely Tuned Cosmos* (Cambridge, UK: Cambridge University Press, 2016), 108. As they further explain, "If gravity were 10^{35} instead of 10^{40} times weaker than the strong force, then the window would close completely. Stable stars would not be possible at all" (109).

20. Lewis and Barnes, *A Fortunate Universe*, 108.

21. Lewis and Barnes, *A Fortunate Universe*, 109–10.

22. Lewis and Barnes, *A Fortunate Universe*, 118. They add a caveat in the next paragraph. Due to some complicating factors in calculating these hypothetical changes, "it may take a slightly higher percentage to totally eradicate carbon or oxygen from the universe." The operative word here, though, is "slightly higher." Even if this turns out to be the case, the degree of strong-force fine tuning for life will remain striking.

23. Fred Hoyle, "The Universe: Past and Present Reflections," *Annual Review of Astronomy and Astrophysics* (1982): 16.

24. Martin Rees, *Just Six Numbers* (New York: Basic Books, 2000), 127.

25. Discovery Science, "Water, Ultimate Giver of Life, Points to Intelligent Design," YouTube, video, 8:05, October 17, 2017, https://www.youtube.com/watch?v=e2i0g1sL-X4. For a deeper look, see Michael Denton, *The Wonder of Water: Water's Profound Fitness for Life on Earth and Mankind* (Seattle, WA: Discovery Institute Press, 2017).

26. For books on the fine-tuning of the universe, see Rees, *Just Six Numbers* and Lewis and Barnes, *A Fortunate Universe*.

27. Freeman Dyson, *Disturbing the Universe* (New York: Basic Books, 1981), 250.

28. See Lewis and Barnes, *A Fortunate Universe*. For a short online overview, see Jay W. Richards, "List of Fine-Tuning Parameters," Discovery Institute Center for Science and Culture, January 14, 2015, https://www.discovery.org/m/securepdfs/2018/12/List-of-Fine-Tuning-Parameters-Jay-Richards.pdf.

29. Simon Friederich, "A New Fine-Tuning Argument for the Multiverse," *Foundations of Physics* 49 (2019): 1012, https://doi.org/10.1007/s10701-019-00246-2.

30. See, for example, physicist Frank Tipler's discussion in the online video segment, *Science Uprising: Fine Tuning* (6:27), https://scienceuprising.com/fine-tuning/.

31. Friederich, "A New Fine-Tuning Argument for the Multiverse," 1012.

32. Friederich, "Fine-Tuning," Stanford Encyclopedia of Philosophy, https://plato.stanford.edu/entries/fine-tuning/.

33. Robin Collins, "The Teleological Argument: An Exploration of the Fine-Tuning of the Universe," *The Blackwell Companion to Natural Theology* [2009] (Chichester, UK: John Wiley & Sons, 2012), 264.

34. Paul Davies, "A Brief History of the Multiverse," *The New York Times*, April 12, 2003, https://www.nytimes.com/2003/04/12/opinion/a-brief-history-of-the-multiverse.html.

2. INFORMATION AND THE ORIGIN OF LIFE

1. *Star Trek: The Next Generation*, season 7, episode 26, "All Good Things," aired May 23, 1994. Excerpt at YouTube, video, 0.46, https://www.youtube.com/watch?v=YLyqTtrhUJE.

2. B. Lee Ligon, "Biography: Louis Pasteur: A Controversial Figure in a Debate on Scientific Ethics," *Seminars in Pediatric Infectious Diseases* 13, no. 2 (April 2002): 134–41.

3. Maxime Schwartz, "The Life and Works of Louis Pasteur," *Journal of Applied Microbiology* 91 (October 2001): 598, https://sfamjournals.onlinelibrary.wiley.com/doi/epdf/10.1046/j.1365-2672.2001.01495.x.

4. Darwin to J.D. Hooker, February 1, 1871, DCP LETT 7471, Darwin Correspondence Project, University of Cambridge, https://www.darwinproject.ac.uk/letter/DCP-LETT-7471.xml. The historical context, as well as additional references in Darwin's letter to Hooker, underscore that speculation about life arising from non-life was not just an isolated musing or offhand remark by Darwin, but was something being actively discussed in the larger scientific community at the time.

5. See for example, "Aleksandr Oparin," *Encyclopedia Britannica*, April 17, 2019, accessed February 10, 2020, https://www.britannica.com/biography/Aleksandr-Oparin.

6. J. B. S. Haldane, "The Origin of Life," *The Rationalist Annual* 148 (1929): 3-10; reprinted in J. B. S. Haldane, *Science and Life: Essays of a Rationalist* (London: Pemberton, 1968).

7. Stanley L. Miller, "A Production of Amino Acids Under Possible Primitive Earth Conditions," *Science* 117 (May 1953): 528–9.

8. George Gaylord Simpson, "The World into Which Darwin Led Us," *Science* 131 (1960): 966–74.

9. Dean H. Kenyon and Gary Steinman, *Biochemical Predestination* (New York: McGraw-Hill, 1969).

10. See, for example, Sidney W. Fox and Klaus Dose, *Molecular Evolution and the Origin of Life*, rev. ed. (1972; repr., New York: Marcel Dekker, 1977), 43; Freeman Dyson, *Origins of Life*, 2nd ed. (Cambridge: Cambridge University Press, 1999), 33–34; and David C. Catling, "Comment on 'A Hydrogen-Rich Early Earth Atmosphere,'" *Science* 311 (2006), author reply 38, https://doi.org/10.1126/science.1117827.

11. See J. P. Ferris and D. E. Nicodem, "Ammonia: Did It Have a Role in Chemical Evolution?" in *The Origin of Life and Evolutionary Biochemistry*, eds. K. Dose, S. W. Fox, G. A. Deborin, and T. E. Pavlovskaya (New York: Plenum Press, 1974), 107; see also a discussion of energy factors impacting the hydrothermal vent hypothesis in J. Baz Jackson, "The 'Origin-of-Life Reactor' and Reduction of CO_2 by H_2 in Inorganic Precipitates," *Journal of Molecular Evolution* 85, no. 1–2 (2017): 1–7, https://doi.org/10.1007/ s00239-017-9805-9.

12. Robert Shapiro, "Prebiotic Cytosine Synthesis: A Critical Analysis and Implications for the Origin of Life, *PNAS* 96, no. 8 (April 1999): 4397–98.

13. See Fox and Dose, *Molecular Evolution and the Origin of Life*, 74–76; and Robert Shapiro, *Origins: A Skeptic's Guide to the Creation of Life on Earth* (New York: Summit Books, 1986), 112.

14. In his book *Icons of Evolution: Science or Myth?* (Washington, DC: Regnery Publishing, 2000), biologist Jonathan Wells reviews in detail the persistence of textbooks overselling the significance of the Miller-Urey experiments. For an updated discussion, see Charles B. Thaxton et al., *The Mystery of Life's Origin: The Continuing Controversy* (Seattle: Discovery Institute Press, 2020), chap. 16.

15. A. G. Cairns-Smith, *Genetic Takeover and the Mineral Origins of Life* (New York: Cambridge University Press, 1982).

16. Charles B. Thaxton, Walter L. Bradley, and Roger L. Olsen, *The Mystery of Life's Origin* (New York: Philosophical Library, 1984).

17. Shigenori Maruyama et al., "Nine Requirements for the Origin of Earth's Life: Not at the Hydrothermal Vent, but in a Nuclear Geyser System," *Geoscience Frontiers* 10, no. 4 (2019): 1337–57, https://doi.org/10.1016/j.gsf.2018.09.011.

18. Sara Imari Walker, "Origins of Life: A Problem for Physics, a Key Issues Review," *Report on Progress in Physics* 80, no. 9 (August 2017), https://doi.org/10.1088/1361-6633/aa7804.

19. Recounted by James D. Watson in *The Double Helix: A Personal Account of the Discovery of the Structure of DNA* (New York: Touchstone, 2001). See also Bill Mesler and H. James Cleaves II, *A Brief History of Creation: Science and the Search for the Origin of Life* (New York: W. W. Norton, 2016), 199–200.

20. James D. Watson and Francis H. C. Crick, "A Structure for Deoxyribose Nucleic Acid," *Nature* 171 (April 1953): 737–38.

21. Jane J. Lee, "Read Francis Crick's $6 Million Letter to Son Describing DNA," *National Geographic Society Newsroom*, National Geographic Society, April 11, 2013, https://blog.nationalgeographic.org/2013/04/11/read-francis-cricks-6-million-letter-to-son-describing-dna/.

22. For a discussion of Crick's remarkable 1957 lecture delivered at a symposium of the Society for Experimental Biology, at University College London, see Matthew Cobb, "60 Years Ago, Francis Crick Changed the Logic of Biology," *PLOS Biology*

15, no. 9 (September 18, 2017): e2003243, https://journals.plos.org/plosbiology/article?id=10.1371/journal.pbio.2003243.

23. Francis H. Crick, "On Protein Synthesis," *Symposia of the Society for Experimental Biology* 12 (1958): 138–63.

24. Stephen C. Meyer, *Signature in the Cell: DNA and the Evidence for Intelligent Design* (New York: HarperOne, 2009), 84.

25. James Tour, "Time Out," *Inference: International Review of Science* 4, no. 4 (July 2019), https://inference-review.com/article/time-out.

26. Meyer, *Signature in the Cell*, 347.

27. Example drawn from Meyer, *Signature in the Cell*, 342. See also "In a Three-Way Radio Debate, Stephen Meyer Takes on a Chemist and a Biologist," March 16, 2016, in *ID the Future*, podcast, MP3 audio, 27:55 (starting at 6:34), www.discovery.org/multimedia/audio/2016/03/in-a-three-way-radio-debate-stephen-meyer-takes-on-a-chemist-and-a-biologist/.

28. For an in-depth analysis of several incorrect arguments often put forward by opponents of intelligent design regarding information in biology, see my series of interviews at *ID the Future*, podcast, MP3 audio, www.discovery.org/multimedia/?s=eric+anderson.

3. A FACTORY THAT BUILDS FACTORIES THAT BUILD FACTORIES THAT...

1. Jack Szostak, "From Telomeres to the Origins of Life," interview by Claudia Dreifus, A Conversation With, *New York Times*, October 17, 2011, https://www.nytimes.com/2011/10/18/science/18conversation.html.

2. Gerald F. Joyce, "In Lab, Clues to How Life Began," interview by Nell Greenfieldboyce, *All Things Considered* (transcript), NPR, January 8, 2009, https://www.npr.org/templates/story/story.php?storyId=99132608.

3. Despite Dawkins's optimistic suggestion that organic molecules would drift "unmolested" through the primordial soup, origin-of-life researchers now recognize that the twin problems of chemical breakdown and interfering cross-reactions pose massive difficulties for any abiogenesis scenario. Indeed, one of the key challenges for modern origin-of-life researchers is to find a way to isolate and protect the tender early molecules from the devastating effects of breakdown and interfering cross-reactions long enough for anything else interesting to happen on the road to life.

4. Richard Dawkins, *The Selfish Gene*, 30th anniversary ed. (New York: Oxford University Press, 2006), 15.

5. Dawkins, *The Selfish Gene*, 15.

6. In 1861, Max Schultze, a German microscopic anatomist, described the cell as "a blob of protoplasm, at the heart of which lies a nucleus...." Félix Dujardin, a French biologist and early pioneer in Protozoa research, referred to a "ubiquitous gelatinous substance" as a key cellular substance in common between animal and plant life. Both quoted in Mario A. Di Gregorio, *From Here to Eternity: Ernst Haeckel and Scientific Faith* (Göttingen, Germany: Vandenhoeck & Ruprecht, 2005), 67–68.

7. Charles Darwin, *The Origin of Species by Means of Natural Selection, or the Preservation of Favoured Races in the Struggle for Life* [1872], 6th ed. (New York: Mentor, 1958). Darwin makes over a half-dozen references to this "plastic" property of organisms in the *Origin*. His glossary defines "plastic" as "readily capable of change."

8. Bradley J. Fikes, "Lab-Evolved Life Gets Closer in Scripps Research Study," *The San Diego Union-Tribune*, August 15, 2016, https://www.sandiegouniontribune.com/business/biotech/sdut-rna-world-origin-life-2016aug15-story.html. The article discusses a science paper by David P. Horning and Gerald F. Joyce, "Amplification of RNA by an RNA polymerase ribozyme," *PNAS* 113, no. 35 (August 2016), https://doi.org/10.1073/pnas.1610103113.

9. See, e.g., Theodosius Dobzhansky's discussion of Gerhard Schramm's "Synthesis of Nucleosides and Polynucleotides with Metaphosphate Esters" in S. W. Fox, ed., *The Origins of Prebiological Systems and of Their Molecular Matrices*, Proceedings of a Conference Conducted at Wakulla Springs, Florida on October 27–30, 1963 (New York: Academic Press, 1965), 309–10.

10. See, for example, Natasha Paul and Gerald F. Joyce, "A Self-Replicating Ligase Ribozyme," *PNAS* 99, no. 20 (October 2002), https://doi.org/10.1073/pnas.202471099.

11. Rice University synthetic organic chemist James Tour recently reviewed some of the challenges of building organic molecules and assembling a self-replicating molecular system, in "Time Out," *Inference: International Review of Science* 4, no. 4 (July 2019), https://inference-review.com/article/time-out. See also Tour's lecture at the 2019 Dallas Science and Faith Conference, at Discovery Science, "James Tour: The Mystery of the Origin of Life," YouTube, video, 58:01, March 18, 2019, https://www.youtube.com/watch?v=zU7Lww-sBPg&t=1644s.

12. To further explore the minimal requirements of a self-replicating entity, see Arminius Mignea, "The Engineering of Life," in *Engineering and the Ultimate: An Interdisciplinary Investigation of Order and Design in Nature and Craft*, eds. Jonathan Bartlett, Dominic Halsmer, and Mark R. Hall (Broken Arrow, OK: Blyth Institute Press, 2014), Part IV.

13. See "RepRap," RepRap, September 22, 2019, accessed November 2, 2019, http://reprap.org/wiki/RepRap; see also "RepRap Project," Wikimedia Foundation, last modified January 5, 2020, 11:07, https://en.wikipedia.org/wiki/RepRap_project.

14. Jean Le Bouthillier, "BI V2.0—A Self-Replicating, High Precision 3D Printer," *Kickstarter*, Kickstarter, PBC, September 22, 2014, accessed November 2, 2019, https://www.kickstarter.com/projects/1784037324/bi-v20-a-self-replicating-high-precision-3d-printe.

15. Several other 3D printing projects have also touted their "self-replicating" capabilities, including Dollo and Snappy.

16. A search for "reprap parts" in Google Images brings up many such examples.

17. Manfred Eigen, "Self-organization of Matter and the Evolution of Biological Macromolecules," *Die Naturwissenschaften* 58, no. 10 (1971): 465–523, https://doi.org/10.1007/BF00623322.

18. Michael J. Denton, *Evolution: A Theory in Crisis* (Chevy Chase, MD: Adler & Adler, 1986), 328–29.

19. John I. Glass et al., "Essential Genes of a Minimal Bacterium," *PNAS* 103, no. 2 (2006): 425–30, https://doi.org/10.1073/pnas.0510013103.

20. Stephen J. Giovannoni et al., "Genome Streamlining in a Cosmopolitan Oceanic Bacterium," *Science* 309, no. 5738 (2005): 1242–45, https://doi.org/10.1126/science.1114057. See also a discussion of efforts to build a minimal genome by the J. Craig Venter Institute at https://www.ncbi.nlm.nih.gov/pmc/articles/PMC4879981/.

21. Consider a minimal cell model discussed by In Vivo Veritas at http://invivoveritasest.blogspot.com/2013/07/a-minimum-cell-model-and-origin-of-life_4.html.

22. This need not be an infinite regress. Based on what we see in biology, the self-replication process apparently can be engineered and the challenge can be overcome. But we do start to sense the scale of the problem.

23. Dawkins, *The Selfish Gene*, 15.

4. IRREDUCIBLE COMPLEXITY AND EVOLUTION

1. For Charles Darwin, there was no goal or purpose in this process; all variations were accidental. Wallace in the end differed in asserting a measure of purposiveness in evolution, as did Asa Gray and others since, but most evolutionary thought has followed Darwin.

2. Darwin himself was unsure whether there was just one original form of life, or a small number of forms (e.g., one ancestor for all plants, one for all animals, one for all fungi), but (at least until very recently) the common view among evolutionary theorists was that there was just one original form.

3. Darwin did not at first call the process of divergence from a common ancestor "evolution" but "descent with modification."

4. For a discussion of some of the difficulties with traditional examples of natural selection, including the peppered moths and Darwin's finches, see Jonathan Wells, *Icons of Evolution: Science or Myth?* (Washington, DC: Regnery Publishing, 2000). See also the companion website at https://iconsofevolution.com/icons-of-evolution/.

5. Yuri Philiptschenko, *Variabilität und Variation* (Berlin: Gebrüder Borntraeger Verlagsbuchhandlung, 1927).

6. Theodosius Dobzhansky, *Genetics and the Origin of Species* [1937] (New York: Columbia University Press, 1982), 12.

7. Winston Ewert, "The Dependency Graph of Life," *BIO-Complexity* 2018, no. 3 (July 17, 2018): 1–27, https://bio-complexity.org/ojs/index.php/main/article/viewFile/BIO-C.2018.3/BIO-C.2018.3.

8. Karl W. Giberson and Francis S. Collins, *The Language of Science and Faith: Straight Answers to Genuine Questions* (Downers Grove, IL: InterVarsity Press, 2011), 43.

9. S. J. Padayatty and M. Levine, "Vitamin C: The Known and the Unknown and Goldilocks," *Oral Diseases* 22, no. 6 (September 2016): 483, https://doi.org/10.1111/odi.12446.

10. See, for example, William A. Dembski, *The Design Revolution: Answering the Toughest Questions about Intelligent Design* (Downers Grove, IL: Intervarsity Press, 2004), 317; see also Jonathan Wells, *The Myth of Junk DNA* (Seattle: Discovery Institute, 2011).

11. Ann K. Gauger, Ola Hössjer, and Colin R. Reeves, "Evidence for Human Uniqueness," in *Theistic Evolution: A Scientific, Philosophical, and Theological Critique*, eds. J.P.

Moreland et al. (Wheaton, IL: Crossway, 2017), 497. [An internal citation was removed from the quotation.]

12. Charles Darwin, *The Origin of Species*, 6th ed. (London: John Murray, 1872), chap. 6, http://darwin-online.org.uk/content/frameset?itemID=F391&viewtype=image&page seq=1.

13. Michael Behe, *Darwin's Black Box: The Biochemical Challenge to Evolution*, 10th anniversary ed. (New York: Free Press, 2006), 39.

14. Behe, *Darwin's Black Box*, 39 (for the quoted phrase), 42–45 (for the discussion of the mousetrap's parts and their interactions).

15. Behe, *Darwin's Black Box*, 51–139.

16. Scott A. Minnich and Stephen C. Meyer, "Genetic Analysis of Coordinate Flagellar and Type III Regulatory Circuits in Pathogenic Bacteria," in *Design and Nature II*, eds. M. W. Collins and C. A. Brebbia (Southampton, UK: WIT Press, 2004), 302. See also the short online video, "Type Three Secretory System," https://revolutionarybehe.com/category/bacterial-flagellum/.

17. Some of these ideas are taken from an excellent interview with Dr. Howard Glicksman, "A Doctor Examines How the Body Meets Its Need for Oxygen," September 27, 2017, in *ID the Future*, podcast, MP3 audio, 17:19, https://www.discovery.org/multimedia/audio/2017/09/a-doctor-examines-how-the-body-meets-its-need-for-oxygen/.

18. Stuart Fox, *Human Physiology*, 15th ed. (New York: McGraw-Hill Education, 2018), 408.

19. According to one analysis, the size of each hemoglobin molecule is approximately 5 nm in diameter. See Harold P. Erickson, "Size and Shape of Protein Molecules at the Nanometer Level Determined by Sedimentation, Gel Filtration, and Electron Microscopy," *Biological Proceedings Online* 11, no. 1, art. 32 (May 15, 2009): 35, https://biologicalproceduresonline.biomedcentral.com/track/pdf/10.1007/s12575-009-9008-x.

20. Douglas Axe, "Estimating the Prevalence of Protein Sequences Adopting Functional Enzyme Folds," *Journal of Molecular Biology* 341 (2004): 1295–1315.

21. Bruce Alberts et al., *Molecular Biology of the Cell*, 6th ed. (New York: Garland Science, 2015), 16.

22. For more information on this evolutionary constraint, see Ann K. Gauger, Stephanie Ebnet, Pamela F. Fahey, and Ralph Seelke, "Reductive Evolution Can Prevent Populations from Taking Simple Adaptive Paths to High Fitness," *BIO-Complexity* 2010, no. 2 (January 2010): 1–9, http://dx.doi.org/10.5048/BIO-C.2010.2.

23. To understand the reason behind the guarded language here, see Mark Gerstein et al., "What Is a Gene, Post-ENCODE?" *Genome Research* 17 (2007): 669-681, https://genome.cshlp.org/content/genome/17/6/669.full.html, as well as Jonathan Wells, *Zombie Science: More Icons of Evolution* (Seattle: Discovery Institute Press, 2017), chap. 4.

24. For a simple explanation and an early animation of protein synthesis, watch *Unlocking the Mystery of Life*, directed by Lad Allen (La Mirada, CA: Illustra Media, 2003), DVD, chapter 10. This portion of the documentary is also available for viewing: Illustra Media, "Unlocking the Mystery of Life (Chapter 10 of 12)," YouTube, video, 4:27, December 9, 2008, https://www.youtube.com/watch?v=gdBJt6sdDfI.

25. For a detailed discussion of several mutations in the flapwing protein (flw) and the impact on fruit fly reproduction, see Shinya Yamamoto et al., "Protein Phosphatase 1ß Limits Ring Canal Constriction during *Drosophila* Germline Cyst Formation," *PLOS ONE* 8, no. 7 (July 25, 2013): e70502, https://doi.org/10.1371/journal.pone.0070502.

26. Michael Behe's follow-up to the bestselling *Darwin's Black Box* examined the experimental evidence and field observations to determine what Darwin's mutation-plus-selection mechanism could actually accomplish. He looked at microbes, since they have huge populations and rapid generational turnover, allowing evolutionary processes to try many millions of mutations over just a few years. From the results he extrapolated mathematically to even longer waiting times and still larger populations. From this work he showed that there are severe limits to the ability of the Darwinian mechanism to effect biological change. It can tinker but not innovate. It can break but not build anything fundamentally new. See Michael J. Behe, *The Edge of Evolution: The Search for the Limits of Darwinism* (New York: Free Press, 2007).

27. Behe has shown that the Darwinian mechanism is most effective as a destructive force, rather than as a creative one. Behe set forth a principle he calls "the first rule of adaptive evolution," which, in essence, states that mutations that yield a net fitness gain are much more likely to be mutations that break or blunt a pre-existing function than ones that produce a new function. See Michael J. Behe, "Experimental Evolution, Loss-of-function Mutations, and 'The First Rule of Adaptive Evolution,'" *The Quarterly Review of Biology* 85, no. 4 (December 2010): 419–45, https://www.lehigh.edu/~inbios/Faculty/Behe/PDF/QRB_paper.pdf. See also his recent book, *Darwin Devolves: The New Science about DNA That Challenges Evolution* (New York: HarperCollins, 2019).

28. Douglas Axe, "Estimating the Prevalence of Protein Sequences Adopting Functional Enzyme Folds." See also Douglas D. Axe, *Undeniable: How Biology Confirms Our Intuition That Life Is Designed* (New York: HarperOne, 2016), 57.

29. Some researchers think the unlikelihood of accidentally forming a protein is even higher than Axe's calculations focused on amino acid sequences. Other factors also required for functional proteins include the free energy states of the amino acid combinations and the stability of the folded protein chain. Recent research hints at additional improbabilities similar to those calculated by Axe. See Brian Miller, "Thermodynamic Challenges to the Origin of Life," in Charles B. Thaxton et al., *The Mystery of Life's Origin: The Continuing Controversy* (Seattle: Discovery Institute Press, 2020), 359–74.

30. The original statement was: "A new scientific truth does not triumph by convincing its opponents and making them see the light, but rather because its opponents eventually die and a new generation grows up that is familiar with it." From Max Planck, *Scientific Autobiography and Other Papers*, trans. Frank Gaynor (London: Williams & Norgate, 1950), 33–34. Others have taken Planck's statement and modified it for brevity, as seen in Pierre Azoulay, Christian Fons-Rosen, and Joshua S. Graff Zivin, "Does Science Advance One Funeral at a Time?," *American Economic Review* 109, no. 8 (2019): 2889–2920. Similar ideas are presented in Thomas Kuhn, *The Structure of Scientific Revolutions*, 4th ed. (Chicago: University of Chicago Press, 2012).

31. See Stephen C. Meyer, *Darwin's Doubt: The Explosive Origin of Animal Life and the Case for Intelligent Design* (New York: HarperOne, 2013), chap. 6.

32. Matti Leisola and Jonathan Witt, *Heretic: One Scientist's Journey from Darwin to Design* (Seattle: Discovery Institute Press, 2018), 84. The paper referred to is Leonidas Salichos and Antonis Rokas, "Inferring Ancient Divergences Requires Genes with Strong Phylogenetic Signals," *Nature* 497 (May 16, 2013): 327–31, https://doi.org/10.1038/nature12130.

33. See Günter Bechly and Stephen C. Meyer, "The Fossil Record and Universal Common Ancestry," in *Theistic Evolution: A Scientific, Philosophical, and Theological Critique*, eds. J. P. Moreland et al. (Wheaton, IL: Crossway, 2017), 331–62

34. "Dissent from Darwin List Tops 1,000—Now the Scientists Weigh In," *Evolution News*, February 14, 2019, https://evolutionnews.org/2019/02/listen-dissent-from-darwin-list-tops-1000-scientists-weigh-in/.

5. Biology's Big Bang: The Cambrian Explosion

1. See "Chengjiang Fossil Site," World Heritage List, UNESCO, accessed February 13, 2020, https://whc.unesco.org/en/list/1388/.

2. See Douglas H. Erwin and James W. Valentine, *The Cambrian Explosion: The Construction of Animal Biodiversity* (Greenwood Village, CO: Roberts and Company, 2013), 330, 324.

3. Christopher J. Lowe, "What Led to Metazoa's Big Bang?" *Science* 340, no. 6137 (2013): 1170–71, https://doi.org/10.1126/science.1237431.

4. Xian-guang Hou et al., *The Cambrian Fossils of Chengjiang, China: The Flowering of Early Animal Life* (Oxford: Blackwell, 2004), 13.

5. D. G. Shu et al., "Lower Cambrian Vertebrates from South China," *Nature* 402 (November 4, 1999): 42–46, https://doi.org/10.1038/46965.

6. Simon Conway Morris and Jean-Bernard Caron, "A Primitive Fish from the Cambrian of North America," *Nature* 512 (June 11, 2014): 419–22, https://doi.org/10.1038/nature13414.

7. John L. Wiester, "Shell Games in California," *Origins Research* 14, no. 2 (1992): 11.

8. Even before Chengjiang, other Cambrian fossil sites around the world, the Burgess Shale especially, already suggested the lawn model of an abrupt appearance of multiple phyla close together in time. But the Chengjiang fossil discoveries made that pattern all the plainer, and the fossils were so well preserved that they created an international sensation, causing the news about the Cambrian explosion to leap well beyond the specialized world of paleontology and evolutionary biology.

9. J. Y. Chen, quoted by Stephen C. Meyer in *Darwin's Doubt: The Explosive Origin of Animal Life and the Case for Intelligent Design* (New York: HarperOne, 2013), 52.

10. See the announcement for the conference on *Evolution: Genetic Novelty/Genomic Variations by RNA Networks and Viruses*, Salzburg, Austria, July 4–8, 2018, http://www.rna-networks.at/about/.

11. Edward J. Steele et al., "Cause of Cambrian Explosion—Terrestrial or Cosmic?" *Progress in Biophysics and Molecular Biology* 136 (August 2018): 3–23, https://doi.org/10.1016/j.pbiomolbio.2018.03.004. Consider also an interview critique with biologist Ann Gauger, "Octopuses from the Sky: Scientists Propose 'Aliens

Seeded Life on Earth,'" July 9, 2018, in *ID the Future*, podcast, MP3 audio, 10:32, https://www.discovery.org/multimedia/?s=outer+space.

12. For Stephen Meyer's extended case on the matter, see *Darwin's Doubt* and *Debating Darwin's Doubt: A Scientific Controversy That Can No Longer Be Denied*, ed. David Klinghoffer (Seattle: Discovery Institute Press, 2015). Other key intelligent design scholars and theorists include Douglas Axe, Michael Behe, William Dembski, Guillermo Gonzalez, Phillip Johnson, Paul Nelson, Jay Richards, and Jonathan Wells. See, for example, a partial list of prominent intelligent design scholars at "Fellows," Discovery Institute Center for Science and Culture, www.discovery.org/id/about/fellows.

13. J. Y. Chen, C. W. Li, Paul Chien, G. Q. Zhou, and Feng Gao, "Weng'an Biota: Casting Light on the Precambrian World" (paper presentation, The Origin of Animal Body Plans and Their Fossil Records, Kunming, China, June 20–26, 1999).

14. Paul Chien, J. Y. Chen, C. W. Li, and Frederick Leung, "SEM Observation of Precambrian Sponge Embryos from Southern China, Revealing Ultrastructures Including Yolk Granules, Secretion Granules, Cytoskeleton, and Nuclei," (paper presentation, North American Paleontological Convention, University of California, Berkeley, June 26–July 1, 2001).

15. John A. Cunningham et al., "The Weng'an Biota (Doushantuo Formation): An Ediacaran Window on Soft-bodied and Multicellular Microorganisms," *Journal of the Geological Society* 174, no. 5 (2017): 793–802, https://doi.org/10.1144/jgs2016-142; David J. Bottjer et al., "Comparative Taphonomy and Phylogenetic Signal of Phosphatized Weng'an and Kuanchuanpu Biotas," *Precambrian Research* (forthcoming). Published ahead of print, August 8, 2019, https://doi.org/10.1016/j.precamres.2019.105408; Jonathan B. Antcliffe et al., "Giving the Early Fossil Record of Sponges a Squeeze," *Biological Reviews* 89, no. 4 (April 29, 2014), https://doi.org/10.1111/brv.12090.

16. Günter Bechly, "Alleged Refutation of the Cambrian Explosion Confirms Abruptness, Vindicates Meyer," Evolution News and Science Today, Discovery Institute, May 29, 2018, https://evolutionnews.org/2018/05/alleged-refutation-of-the-cambrian-explosion-confirms-abruptness-vindicates-meyer/.

17. Stephen Q. Dornbos et al., "A New Burgess Shale-Type Deposit from the Ediacaran of Western Mongolia," *Scientific Reports* 6 (2016): 23438; Xunlai Yuan et al., "An Early Ediacaran Assemblage of Macroscopic and Morphologically Differentiated Eukaryotes," *Nature* 470 (2011): 390-3.

18. Allison C. Daley et al., "Early Fossil Record of Euarthropoda and the Cambrian Explosion," *PNAS* 115, no. 21 (2018): 5323-31.

19. Meyer, *Darwin's Doubt*, 85-6.

20. Giulio Mariotti et al., "Microbial Origin of Early Animal Trace Fossils," *Journal of Sedimentary Research*, 86 (2016): 287–93.

21. Erwin and Valentine, *The Cambrian Explosion*, 6.

22. Martin Scheffer, *Critical Transitions in Nature and Society* (Princeton, NJ: Princeton University Press, 2009), 169-70.

ABOUT THE AUTHORS

Thomas Y. Lo, PhD, is an engineer and entrepreneur focused on medical and fitness wearable technology development. The president and CTO of Logos Care, Inc., he received his PhD in electrical engineering from the University of Illinois.

Paul K. Chien, PhD, is professor emeritus at the University of San Francisco, where he was formerly chairman of the Department of Biology. He also has taught at the Chinese University of Hong Kong, consulted for the California Institute of Technology's Kerckhoff Marine Laboratory, and served as a scanning electron microscopy analyst for the Biology Department of Santa Clara University, California. Chien has published with colleagues from several institutions throughout China. He received his PhD in biology from the University of California at Irvine.

Eric H. Anderson, JD, J. Reuben Clark Law School, is an entrepreneur, software engineering executive, design theorist, and contributing author on evolution and intelligent design at Uncommon Descent.

Robert A. Alston, PhD, is an electrical engineer with Picatinny Arsenal and a former NASA special projects engineer. He received his PhD in electrical engineering from North Carolina Agricultural and Technical State University.

Robert P. Waltzer, PhD, is professor and chair of the Department of Biology at Belhaven University in Jackson, Mississippi. He served as co-chair of the History and Philosophy of Science Section at Mississippi Academy of Sciences, and received his PhD in anatomy with a focus on neuroanatomy from Ohio State University.

IMAGE CREDITS

1. THE BIG BANG AND THE FINE-TUNED UNIVERSE

Figure 1.1. Albert Einstein. Photograph by Ferdinand Shmutzer, 1921. Modified by Quibik, 2012, Wikimedia Commons. Public domain.

Figure 1.2. Holmdel horn antenna at Bell Labs. Photograph by NASA, 1962. Public domain.

Figure 1.3. Big Bang Expansion. "Timeline of the Universe." Image by NASA/WMAP Science Team. Public domain.

2. INFORMATION AND THE ORIGIN OF LIFE

Figure 2.1. Primordial landscape. "Chemical Soups around Cool Stars." Illustration by NASA/JPL-Caltech. Public domain.

Figure 2.2. Rendering of the setup used in the Miller-Urey experiment. Adapted by Brian Gage from various images, including image by Yassine Mrabet, 2008, Wikimedia Commons. CC BY-SA license.

Figure 2.3. DNA structure. "DNA Replication Split." Image by Madeleine Price Ball (Madprime), 2013, Wikimedia Commons. CCO 1.0 license.

3. A FACTORY THAT BUILDS FACTORIES THAT BUILD FACTORIES THAT...

Figure 3.1. 3D printed cube stand. Photographs by Eric H. Anderson.

Figure 3.2. RepRap printer. Image by RepRap Project, 2007, Wikimedia Commons. CC BY-SA 3.0 license. Descriptive arrows added.

4. IRREDUCIBLE COMPLEXITY AND EVOLUTION

Figure 4.1. Tree of Life. "Genealogical Tree of Humanity." Illustration by Ernst Haeckel, ca. 1877. Modified by Fuelbottle, 2007, Wikimedia Commons. Public domain.

Figure 4.2. Galapagos finches. Illustration by John Gould in Charles Darwin, *Journal of Researches into the Natural History and Geology of the Countries Visited during the Voyage of H. M. S. Beagle round the World* (London: John Murray, 1845), 379. Modified by Shyamal, Wikimedia Commons. Public domain.

Figure 4.3. Common mousetrap. Image by Eric H. Anderson.

Figure 4.4. Electron micrograph of a bacterium. Transmission electron micrograph by Graham Bradley, 2005, Wikimedia Commons. Public domain.

Figure 4.5. Bacterial flagellum. Illustration by Joseph Condeelis/Light Productions. Adapted by Brian Gage.

Figure 4.6. Alveolar sacs and pulmonary capillaries. Image by LadyofHats and Salman666, 2007, Wikimedia Commons. Public domain.

5. Biology's Big Bang—The Cambrian Explosion

Figure 5.1. Paul K. Chien in front of Maotian Shan. Photograph by Illustra Media. Used with permission.

Figures 5.2–5.3. Stellostomites and Hyoliths. Photographs by Paul K. Chien.

Figure 5.4. Maotianshania cylindrica. Photograph by Illustra Media. Used with permission.

Figures 5.5–5.6. Leanchoilia and trilobite. Photograph by Illustra Media. Used with permission.

Figure 5.7. Haikouella. Photograph by Paul K. Chien.

Figure 5.8. Phyla graphic. Recreation by Eric H. Anderson, based on information provided by D. G. Shu to the author.

Figure 5.9. Graphical representation of the "Hard Facts Wall" and actual data. Image by Access Research Network. Used with permission.

Figure 5.10. California Academy of Sciences museum display of the "Timeline of Life on Earth." Photograph by Paul K. Chien.

Figure 5.11. Panel from exhibit at the Beijing National Museum of Natural History. Photograph by Paul K. Chien.

Figure 5.12. Small round fossils. Photograph by Paul K. Chien.

Figure 5.13. Sponge egg images. Photographs by Paul K. Chien.

Recommended Resources
for Digging Deeper

1. *The Privileged Planet* by Guillermo Gonzalez and Jay Richards
2. *The Privileged Planet* film by Illustra Media
3. *A Fortunate Universe: Life in a Finely Tuned Cosmos* by Geraint Lewis and Luke Barnes
4. *Signature in the Cell* by Stephen Meyer
5. *The Mystery of Life's Origin: The Continuing Controversy* by Charles Thaxton et al.
6. Dallas Science and Faith Conference, James Tour: *The Mystery of the Origin of Life* at the Discovery Science YouTube channel
7. *Darwin's Black Box*, revised edition, by Michael Behe
8. *Secrets of the Cell* at michaelbehe.com
9. *Revolutionary, The Information Enigma,* and other origins videos at the Discovery Science YouTube channel
10. *Icons of Evolution* by Jonathan Wells
11. *Zombie Science* by Jonathan Wells, and iconsofevolution.com
12. *Darwin Devolves* by Michael Behe
13. *Darwin's Doubt* by Stephen Meyer
14. *Debating Darwin's Doubt*, ed. David Klinghoffer
15. *Darwin's Dilemma* by Illustra Media, a film exploring the Cambrian explosion as evidence for intelligent design. (A Chinese version was recently made available at the Illustra Media YouTube channel.)

INDEX